CORPSE TALK

TALK

Ground-Breaking

SCIENTISTS

BY ADAM AND LISA MURPHY

CONTENTS

VON HUMBOLDT
EXPLORER, NATURALIST, GEOGRAPHER, ETC... 1769–1859

68

JAMES BARRY
DOCTOR 1790s–1865

72

CHARLES DARWIN
NATURALIST 1809–1882

78

DMITRI MENDELEEV
CHEMIST 1834–1907

88

MARIE CURIE
CHEMIST & PHYSICIST 1867–1934

94

GEORGE WASHINGTON CARVER
BOTANIST & INVENTOR 1860s–1943

98

NIKOLA TESLA
INVENTOR 1856–1943

104

ALAN TURING
COMPUTER SCIENTIST 1912–1954

110

ALBERT EINSTEIN
PHYSICIST 1879–1955

116

MY FIRST GUEST IS QUITE POSSIBLY THE MOST IMPORTANT THINKER OF **ALL TIME!** WHEN HE WASN'T BUSY DEFINING THE GROUND RULES OF PHILOSOPHY, HE WAS OFF INVENTING A LITTLE THING CALLED **SCIENCE**, WHICH YOU MIGHT HAVE HEARD OF.

HE'S A THINKER SO **IMPORTANT,** THEY JUST CALLED HIM "THE PHILOSOPHER" – THAT'S RIGHT, IT'S...

ARISTOTLE!

ARISTOTLE
PHILOSOPHER
384–322 BCE

ARISTOTLE, IN ANCIENT GREECE, PHILOSOPHY WAS PRETTY MUCH A **FULL-CONTACT SPORT,** WITH NEW SCHOOLS AND IDEAS ALL FIGHTING FOR SUPREMACY.

FOR SURE. AND THE ABSOLUTE TOP DOG WAS MY TEACHER, **PLATO.** (AT LEAST UNTIL I CAME ALONG!)

PLATO

ARI

PLATO'S WHOLE PHILOSOPHICAL SYSTEM WAS BUILT ON THE IDEA THAT THERE ARE THESE PURE, UNCHANGING, PERFECT IDEALS — OR FORMS — WHICH ONLY EXIST IN HEAVEN, OR THE MIND OF THE PHILOSOPHER.

SO, FOR EXAMPLE, THERE ARE LOTS OF **TRIANGLES** IN THE WORLD AND NONE OF THEM ARE PERFECT. THEY'LL ALWAYS BE WONKY OR SKEWY IN SOME WAY...

BUT EACH OF THEM IS AN **IMPERFECT COPY** OF THE PERFECT **IDEA** OF "TRIANGLE", WHICH WE CAN ONLY EVER SEE IN OUR MINDS...

AND IT'S THE SAME FOR OTHER ABSTRACT IDEALS, LIKE TRUTH OR JUSTICE OR BEAUTY; THEY MIGHT NEVER BE PERFECT IN **THIS** WORLD, BUT THEY **DO** EXIST IN A PLACE **BEYOND HEAVEN**...

WHICH, I'LL BE HONEST, ALWAYS STRUCK ME AS A LOAD OF OLD **COBBLERS**.

THE WORLD'S NOT PERFECT; IT'S WEIRD AND WONKY AND DIRTY AND UGLY AND MESSY. BUT THINGS HAPPEN FOR **REASONS**.

INSTEAD OF THESE SILLY BRAIN GAMES, WHY CAN'T THERE BE **REAL** REASONS WHY THINGS ARE THE WAY THEY ARE?

UH. YOU LOST ME...

OK. HERE'S A BASIC QUESTION: WHY DO SOME ANIMALS HAVE NECKS, AND SOME NOT?

UH... DON'T THEY ALL?

NO! FISH DON'T! NOR DO OCTOPUSES!

I STARTED THINKING MAYBE THERE'S SOMETHING THAT **CAUSES** SOME ANIMALS TO HAVE NECKS. NOT BECAUSE IT'S BEAUTIFUL, OR WHATEVER, BUT A REAL, PHYSICAL CAUSE IN THE REAL WORLD.

IF WE WANT TO UNDERSTAND THINGS, WE CAN'T JUST **THINK** ABOUT THEM. WE HAVE TO **STUDY** THEM.

AND SO THAT'S EXACTLY WHAT YOU DID. YOU CONDUCTED DETAILED DISSECTIONS ON ALL SORTS OF ANIMALS, BIRDS AND SEA CREATURES TO TRY AND GET A CLEAR SENSE OF THEIR SIMILARITIES AND DIFFERENCES.

NO ONE ELSE AT THE ACADEMY WAS DOING THAT! THEY WERE TOO BUSY THINKING ABOUT TRUTH AND BEAUTY TO SPEND THEIR TIME CUDDLING ABOUT IN OCTOPUS GUTS!

AND DO YOU KNOW WHAT I FOUND?

I HAVE A FEELING YOU'RE GOING TO TELL ME...

ALL ANIMALS WITH NECKS HAVE LUNGS!

AND VICE VERSA.

MAYBE LUNGS **CAUSE** NECKS! OR NECKS CAUSE LUNGS... HM...

SO, YOUR BIG IDEA IS TO NOT JUST MAKE UP STORIES, BUT TO LOOK AT THINGS TO SEE IF YOU'RE RIGHT?

JUST SEEMS KINDA... OBVIOUS...

TO YOU, MAYBE! YOU'VE HAD **2,500** YEARS TO GET USED TO IT! I WAS THE **FIRST PERSON** TO THINK LIKE THIS!

HOLD ON, GO BACK A STEP. WHEN YOU SAY **ALL** ANIMALS... HOW'D YOU **KNOW**? DID YOU DISSECT EVERY ANIMAL THERE IS!?

PRETTY CLOSE. ONE OF MY STUDENTS WENT ON TO CONQUER MOST OF THE WORLD AS **ALEXANDER THE GREAT.**

DID YOU... UH... REMEMBER YOUR HOMEWORK?

AND HE ALSO HELPED ME CONQUER THE WORLD OF **KNOWLEDGE**, BY TAKING ALONG AN ARMY OF COLLECTORS WHO BROUGHT BACK AS MANY DIFFERENT PLANT AND ANIMAL SAMPLES AS THEY COULD CARRY.

OOH! I'VE NEVER SEEN **THAT** BEETLE BEFORE, HAVE YOU!?

YEAH, GOOD TIMES, GOOD TIMES...

YOUR OBSERVATIONS WERE SO AMAZINGLY ACCURATE, IT WAS **THOUSANDS** OF YEARS BEFORE SCIENCE CAUGHT UP!

YOUR THEORIES ABOUT CUTTLEFISH REPRODUCTION, FOR EXAMPLE, WEREN'T CONFIRMED UNTIL **1959**! THAT'S A LONG TIME!

GREAT SCOTT! ARISTOTLE WAS RIGHT!

IN FACT, YOUR RESULTS WERE **SO** GOOD, THEY ACTUALLY HELD SCIENCE **BACK** FOR THOUSANDS OF YEARS.

INSTEAD OF STUDYING THE WORLD AROUND THEM, PEOPLE JUST TOOK YOUR WORD FOR IT!

WHAT?! BUT THAT'S **EXACTLY** WHAT I TOLD THEM **NOT** TO DO!

AND I NEVER CLAIMED I'D GOT **EVERYTHING** RIGHT...

LIKE THE WHOLE INSECTS-APPEARING-OUT-OF-NOWHERE THING?

AH, NUTS. NOT THE INSECTS THING...

I OBSERVED YOUNG INSECTS HATCHING OUT OF **FRESH POOP**, EVEN WHEN I'D BEEN **VERY CAREFUL** TO MAKE SURE NO ADULT INSECTS HAD LAID THEIR EGGS IN IT.

AH, BUT THERE COULD HAVE BEEN EGGS ALREADY IN THE POOPING ANIMAL'S **DIGESTIVE TRACT!**

BAH. DIDN'T THINK OF THAT...

THE TRUE STORY WASN'T DISCOVERED UNTIL MARIA SIBYLLA MERIAN IN THE **17**TH CENTURY!*

BUT HEY, DON'T WORRY. WE CAUGHT UP EVENTUALLY!

*SEE PAGE **32**

AND TODAY YOU'RE REVERED, NOT JUST AS THE FATHER OF SCIENCE, BUT ALSO LOGIC, ETHICS, POLITICAL THEORY, PHILOSOPHY AND EVEN WRITING!

WHOA. NICE PECS!

HOLLYWOOD SCRIPTWRITERS STUDY YOUR BOOK ON **DRAMA** LIKE IT WAS **THE BIBLE** FOR TIPS ON HOW TO STRUCTURE THE STORIES OF THEIR MOVIES!

HM... WHAT DID ARISTOTLE SAY?

JUST THE DRAMA? WHAT ABOUT MY BOOK ON **COMEDY?**

NOT ALL OF YOUR WRITINGS SURVIVED - IT **WAS** A LONG TIME AGO, AFTER ALL...

BUT SINCE YOU'RE HERE, YOU DON'T HAVE A FUNNY ENDING, BY ANY CHANCE...?

HEY, IT'S **YOUR** COMIC...

SCHOOL OF LIFE

KING HIERON OF SYRACUSE HAD A GOLD CROWN MADE, BUT HE WAS AFRAID THE GOLDSMITH HAD CHEATED HIM BY MIXING IN SOME CHEAPER SILVER.

HEH HEH HEH

1KG OF SILVER TAKES UP **MORE SPACE** THAN 1KG OF GOLD, SO THE EASY SOLUTION WOULD BE TO MELT IT DOWN AND MAKE A COMPARISON.

BUT THIS CROWN WAS A **SACRED OFFERING** TO THE GODS. IT COULDN'T BE DAMAGED!

MMM. QUITE A PICKLE...

YOU'RE MY MATHEMATICIAN! **UNPICKLE** IT!

MAN! I SPENT **AGES** TRYING TO FIGURE THAT ONE OUT!

WAIT! YOU COULD...

NO.

MAYBE...

NO, NO, THAT'LL NEVER WORK!

HMMM.

HOW ABOUT..?

BUT THEN, THE ANSWER CAME TO ME WHERE I LEAST EXPECTED IT... IN THE BATH!

THE TUB WAS FULL, SO WHEN I GOT IN, WATER GOT **OUT**.

I COULD DO THE SAME WITH THE CROWN! IF IT CONTAINED SILVER, IT WOULD **DISPLACE** MORE WATER THAN THE SAME WEIGHT OF PURE GOLD...

AND IN MY ENTHUSIASM, IT'S POSSIBLE I MAY HAVE OMITTED TO PUT MY CLOTHES ON...

EUREKA!

YOU ALSO INVENTED LOTS OF OTHER THINGS; LIKE THE **LEVER**!

I DIDN'T ACTUALLY **INVENT** IT, PER SE, BUT EXPLAINED THE MATHEMATICS OF HOW IT WORKS, WHICH IS KIND OF **MORE** AWESOME, IF YOU THINK ABOUT IT...

IF YOU HAVE TWO THINGS OF **EQUAL WEIGHT**, YOU CAN BALANCE THEM ON A CENTRAL POINT...

BUT IF ONE SIDE IS **HEAVIER**, IT WILL PUSH THE OTHER SIDE UP.

IF YOU MOVE THE CENTRE POINT THOUGH, YOU CAN **BALANCE** LIGHT AND HEAVY THINGS.

OR EVEN **LIFT** HEAVY THINGS. I USED TO SAY, "GIVE ME A LONG ENOUGH LEVER, AND I'LL MOVE THE **WORLD**."

WHOA! WHOA! I'M NOT **THAT** HEAVY!

AND THAT WAS ALSO THE PRINCIPLE BEHIND YOUR ANCIENT **SECRET** WEAPONS!

YOU **REALLY** WANNA HEAR ABOUT THAT!?

I COULD EXPLAIN SOMETHING EVEN **MORE** AWESOME. LIKE MY PROOF THAT THE VOLUME OF A SPHERE IS 2/3 THAT OF A CYLINDER OF EQUAL HEIGHT...?

NO. PLEASE. THE SECRET WEAPONS...

-SIGH- OK... SO, FOR YEARS, KING HIERON HAD BEEN PLAYING THE **ROMANS** AND THE **CARTHAGINIANS** OFF AGAINST ONE ANOTHER.

BUT THEN HE DIED, AND WE GOT SUCKED INTO THE WAR, WHICH MEANT A MASSIVE ROMAN ARMY SET OUT TO CONQUER US.

HEH HEH! BUT THEY DIDN'T RECKON ON YOUR SECRET SCIENCE WEAPONS...

LIKE THE **SHIP SHAKER**! IF ANY SHIP GOT TOO CLOSE TO THE WALLS, A HUGE **GRAPPLING HOOK** SHOT OUT AND ATTACHED TO IT...

AND THEN, USING THE PRINCIPLES OF **LEVERAGE**, IT WAS PULLED AROUND UNTIL IT SANK!

PLUS THE **DEATH RAY**!

OH, **MAN**. YOU KNOW IT'S NOT EVEN PROVEN I **INVENTED** THAT...

DUDE.

DEATH.

RAY.

OK, FINE.

THE IDEA WAS BASICALLY A HUGE ARRAY OF BRONZE **MIRRORS**...

IF THEY WERE ALL ANGLED CORRECTLY, THEY WOULD REFLECT AND CONCENTRATE THE SUN'S RAYS, MAKING THE SHIPS BURST INTO FLAMES.

HOO! SO AWESOME!

FOR **TWO LONG YEARS** MY MACHINES KEPT THE MIGHTY ROMAN ARMY AT BAY...

BUT IN THE END, THEY **CHEATED**, AND SNUCK INTO THE CITY WHILE EVERYONE WAS BUSY AT THE FESTIVAL OF ARTEMIS...

I WAS ABSORBED WITH MORE PRESSING BUSINESS— A **TOTALLY SWEET** MATHEMATICAL PROBLEM.

OI! YOU!

PLEASE! DON'T DISTURB MY CIRCLES...

DOO DOO DE DOO

DOESN'T LIKE BEING IGNORED.

DOO DOO DE DOO

YOU WERE **CRUELLY SLAIN** BY AN IMPATIENT LEGIONARY!

AND I WAS **THIS** CLOSE TO THE ANSWER!

17

SO I DEVELOPED A NEW TECHNIQUE. FIRST YOU DEVELOP A **HYPOTHESIS**...

A HYPOTHE-WHAT?

HYPOTHESIS. IT'S JUST A STORY OF HOW YOU THINK THINGS WORK.

OK, HERE'S A HYPOTHESIS: YOUR GLASSES ARE INDESTRUCTABLE...

MAY I?

I SUBJECT THE HYPOTHESIS TO **EXPERIMENT**, AND TEST IT OVER AND OVER AGAIN.

THERE. **HYPOTHESIS** DISPROVED!

BUT IF I **CAN'T** DISPROVE IT, THEN IT'S POSSIBLE THE HYPOTHESIS IS **TRUE**.

I AM QUITE SURE YOU COULD HAVE USED A LESS... VIOLENT EXAMPLE.

YOUR AH... FAME AS A SCIENTIST SPREAD, TAKING YOU FROM YOUR HOMETOWN OF BASRA IN IRAQ ALL THE WAY TO EGYPT...

OH, RIGHT. SO, THE THING IS, THE WHOLE OF EGYPT WAS DEPENDENT ON THE **NILE RIVER**: EACH YEAR IT WOULD FLOOD AND WATER THE FIELDS...

ONLY, SOME YEARS IT WOULDN'T RISE ENOUGH, AND ALL THE CROPS WOULD DIE.

BUT OTHER YEARS IT WOULD RISE TOO MUCH AND SWEEP AWAY EVERYONE'S HOUSES.

SO, I CAME UP WITH THIS GREAT PLAN TO USE **SCIENCE** TO BUILD A DAM ACROSS THE RIVER, TO CONTROL HOW MUCH WATER CAME DOWN.

I EVEN HAD THE SPOT CHOSEN AND EVERYTHING. ONLY, WHEN I GOT THERE, I REALISED THERE WAS NO **WAY** WE COULD BUILD A DAM BIG ENOUGH TO CONTROL THAT RIVER!

ER...

WELL, THAT'S JUST SCIENCE, RIGHT?

HYPOTHESIS DISPROVED!

YEEAH... EXCEPT I'D KINDA ALREADY PROMISED THE CALIPH OF EGYPT THAT I COULD DO IT.

BEAR IN MIND THIS WAS THE GUY THEY CALLED THE **MAD CALIPH** BECAUSE HE HAD A TENDENCY TO RANDOMLY **KILL** PEOPLE IF THEY CHEESED HIM OFF.

THIS WAS ALSO THE GUY WHO'D ONCE ORDERED ALL THE **DOGS** IN CAIRO TO BE **EXECUTED** BECAUSE THEIR BARKING ANNOYED HIM.

SO WHEN I BROKE THE NEWS, I WAS PRETTY SURE HE WASN'T JUST GOING TO SAY "HYPOTHESIS DISPROVED" AND MOVE ON.

BUT DON'T WORRY, I HAD A PLAN...

THE GREAT CALIPH WILL SEE YOU NOW...

WEEBLE WIBBLE!

THAT WAS YOUR AWESOME PLAN!? PRETENDING TO BE **MAD**!?

HEY, IT WORKED! INSTEAD OF BEING EXECUTED I GOT OFF WITH **HOUSE ARREST**!

SO BASICALLY, I GOT TO STAY HOME AND WORK ON SCIENCE, BUT WITH **NO INTERRUPTIONS**!

AND DON'T EVEN THINK ABOUT ESCAPING!

AND IT WAS THEN THAT YOU MANAGED TO EXPLAIN, FOR THE FIRST TIME EVER, THE REAL SCIENCE OF **LIGHT** AND OF **SIGHT**.

WELL, I WAS STILL THINKING ABOUT THE GREEKS AND THEIR CRAZY THEORIES. LIKE, THEY HAD ONE IDEA THAT LIGHT SHOOTS **OUT** OF YOUR EYES TO LIGHT UP WHATEVER YOU'RE LOOKING AT...

WELL, I HAD A PRETTY GOOD WAY OF TESTING THAT: CLOSE THE SHUTTERS!

HYPOTHESIS **DISPROVED**!

BUT THEN I NOTICED A RAY OF LIGHT COMING IN THROUGH A LITTLE HOLE IN MY SHUTTERS.

AND **THEN** I SAW SOMETHING **REALLY** WEIRD — ON THE OPPOSITE WALL, I COULD SEE WHAT WAS OUTSIDE, ONLY IT WAS **UPSIDE DOWN**!

NOW, THERE'S ONLY **ONE** THEORY THAT COULD EXPLAIN **THAT**!

REALLY?

I MEAN, YES! OBVIOUSLY!

ER... WHAT IS IT...?

LIGHT MUST BE TRAVELLING IN A **STRAIGHT LINE** FROM THE SUN, AND THEN BOUNCING OFF THE OBJECTS OUTSIDE.

ANYBODY LOOKING AT SOMETHING WILL HAVE **SOME** OF THOSE RAYS BOUNCING IN THEIR DIRECTION, ALLOWING THEM TO SEE IT.

BUT ONLY A FEW RAYS GET THROUGH THE LITTLE HOLE.

THIS TOP RAY

ENDS UP AT THE BOTTOM.

WHICH IS WHY THE IMAGE IS UPSIDE DOWN.

AND I ALSO REALISED IT'S THE SAME THING THAT'S HAPPENING IN YOUR EYE!

SIGNAL TO BRAIN.

LITTLE HOLE

LANDS ON BACK OF EYE.

LIGHT GOES IN.

AND IT'S THE SAME THING THAT HAPPENS IN A **CAMERA**, ONLY WITH SOME HIGH-TECH ADDED EXTRAS...

THE **WORD** "CAMERA" IS SHORT FOR **CAMERA OBSCURA**, LATIN FOR "DARK ROOM"!

SO NOW, IF YOU COULD JUST USE YOUR OCULAR ABILITIES TO **FIX THESE GLASSES**...

SORRY, GLASSES WEREN'T INVENTED FOR ANOTHER TWO CENTURIES.

BUT **I** HAD ANOTHER IDEA. I WOULD USE THIS NEW INVENTION TO PROBE THE SECRETS OF THE **UNIVERSE!**

SEEN UP CLOSE, I REALISED THAT THOSE GREY SPLOTCHES ON THE MOON ARE REALLY **SHADOWS** CAST BY MASSIVE MOUNTAIN RANGES!

I FOUND A COLLECTION OF TINY LIGHTS THAT I REALISED WERE **OTHER MOONS,** CIRCLING THE VAST PLANET **JUPITER.**

AND, MOST STRIKINGLY, I SAW THE PLANET **VENUS** UP CLOSE. TURNS OUT, IT HAS **PHASES,** JUST LIKE OUR MOON!

BUT THAT WAS KIND OF A PROBLEM. EVERYONE BELIEVED THE **EARTH** WAS THE CENTRE OF THE UNIVERSE, AND EVERYTHING ELSE CIRCLED AROUND IT.

VENUS
SUN
EARTH
DOME OF FIXED STARS

WHAT? NO! THE **EARTH** GOES AROUND THE **SUN!**

DOESN'T IT...?

WELL, THAT'S WHAT MY FINDINGS SUGGESTED.

IT'S NOT **POSSIBLE** FOR THE SUN TO CAST THOSE SHADOWS ON VENUS IF THEY BOTH GO ROUND THE EARTH.

BUT THIS WAS THE **TOTAL OPPOSITE** OF WHAT EVERYONE HAD BELIEVED FOR **THOUSANDS** OF YEARS!

THE CHURCH GOT WIND OF IT, AND THEY STARTED **FREAKING OUT.**

WHAT HAS THE **CHURCH** GOT TO DO WITH IT?

ARE YOU KIDDING? BACK THEN, THE CHURCH HAD **EVERYTHING** TO DO WITH **EVERYTHING!**

AND THEY WERE PARTICULARLY CONCERNED THAT THIS NEW THEORY **CONTRADICTED** SOME PASSAGES IN THE BIBLE.

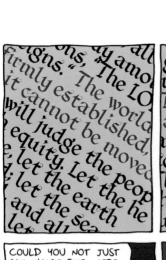

firmly established, it cannot be moved... He will judge the peoples with equity. Let the heavens... let the earth... and all... let...

...and generation go, but the earth remains forever. The sun also arises, and sets, and hurries back to where it rises. The wind blows to the south and turns to the n...

HOLY SCRIPTURE CAN'T **POSSIBLY** BE WRONG! IT **MUST** BE THESE NEW THEORIES!

COULD YOU NOT JUST SAY THOSE BITS WERE "POETICAL" OR SOMETHING?

I TRIED THAT.

POETICAL? TRY **HERETICAL**.

A HERETIC WAS SOMEONE WHO BELIEVED **ILLEGAL IDEAS** WHICH WERE BANNED BY THE CHURCH.

AND THEY HAD A **SPECIAL PUNISHMENT** RESERVED FOR THAT...

SO I KEPT QUIET ABOUT MY FINDINGS, BUT THEN AN OLD BUDDY OF MINE GOT ELECTED **POPE**.

IT'S COOL, GG. WHY DON'T YOU WRITE A BOOK THAT EXPLAINS **BOTH SIDES**, LET PEOPLE DECIDE FOR THEMSELVES...

BUT THAT'S... NOT REALLY WHAT YOU DID...

SURE IT IS! MY BOOK HAD TWO CHARACTERS. EACH PUTTING FORWARD ONE SIDE OF THE ARGUMENT.

YEAH, BUT YOU MADE THE SUN-GOES-AROUND-THE-EARTH GUY SOUND REALLY **STUPID**.

ANYONE WHO BELIEVES THAT **IS** REALLY STUPID!

AND YOU CALLED HIM "SIMPLICIO", MEANING SIMPLETON!

IT'S THE NAME OF AN ANCIENT GREEK PHILOSOPHER!

WELL, THE POPE THOUGHT YOU WERE MAKING FUN OF HIM IN PUBLIC.

WHAT THE HEY, G!? I THOUGHT WE WERE FRIENDS...

YOU WERE SUMMONED TO APPEAR BEFORE THE CHURCH'S DREADED SECRET POLICE, THE **INQUISITION**.

BAH! YOU FOOLS CAN NEVER HOLD BACK **SCIENCE!** THE **TRUTH** SHALL OVERCOME!

AH... YEEAH... ALL THAT STUFF JUST NOW...

DIDN'T MEAN IT... THE EARTH IS TOTALLY STATIONARY.

TOTALLY.

OOH. **VERY** PRINCIPLED, MR HERO-OF-SCIENCE!

ARE YOU KIDDING? **HELLOO!? TORTURE!!?**

ANYWAY, WHO CARES WHAT THEY SAY, OR WHAT **I** SAY. THE TRUTH IS THE TRUTH. AND THE EARTH **DOES** GO AROUND THE SUN.

THEY PUT YOU UNDER HOUSE ARREST FOR THE REST OF YOUR LIFE.

BUT, YOU KNOW WHAT? NOT A PROBLEM! GAVE ME MORE TIME TO FINISH UP MY MASTERPIECES...

TWO **OTHER** BOOKS ABOUT WHY THE ANCIENT WISDOM IS ALL WRONG AND SCIENCE IS **AWESOME**!

SECRETS of the SOLAR SYSTEM

WOO! MY TELESCOPE ALLOWED ME TO REACH OUT INTO THE ICY VASTNESS OF SPACE, AND UNLOCK THE SECRETS OF THE SOLAR SYSTEM!

THE SUN
BY FAR THE LARGEST BODY IN THE SOLAR SYSTEM. AT ITS CORE, THE GRAVITY IS SO INTENSE IT CAUSES A NUCLEAR FUSION REACTION THAT REACHES **15** MILLION °C!

VENUS
POISONOUS GREENHOUSE GASSES HAVE MADE VENUS THE HOTTEST PLANET, WITH AN ATMOSPHERE OF OVER **400**°C.

BY OBSERVING SUNSPOTS MOVING ON THE SURFACE OF THE SUN, I WAS ABLE TO DEDUCE THAT THE SUN ITSELF IS SPINNING.

IT WAS MY OBSERVATIONS OF THE PHASES OF VENUS THAT FIRST LED ME TO CONCLUDE THAT THE EARTH ORBITS THE SUN, NOT THE OTHER WAY ROUND.

THE MOON
EARTH'S ROCKY SATELLITE IS COVERED IN CRATERS FROM ANCIENT ASTEROID IMPACTS.

EARTH
OUR HOME. EARTH IS THE ONLY PLANET IN THE SOLAR SYSTEM THAT WE KNOW SUSTAINS LIFE, THANKS TO ITS HIGH WATER CONTENT AND OXYGEN-RICH ATMOSPHERE.

JUPITER
THE LARGEST PLANET BY FAR, JUPITER IS A GIGANTIC BALL OF GAS. THE GREAT RED SPOT IS A MASSIVE ANTICYCLONE STORM, FUELLED BY THE HOT GASSES OF THE INTERIOR.

SATURN
THE FAMOUS RINGS OF SATURN ARE COMPOSED OF ROCK, DUST AND ICE. MY TELESCOPE WASN'T QUITE GOOD ENOUGH TO MAKE THEM OUT — I THOUGHT THEY WERE 2 MOONS, ONE ON EITHER SIDE OF THE PLANET.

JUPITER HAS **69 MOONS**, THANKS TO ITS ENORMOUS GRAVITATIONAL PULL. THE LARGEST **4** WERE FIRST OBSERVED BY -AHEM- GALILEIO.

ASTEROID BELT
MILLIONS OF FLOATING SPACE ROCKS — THEY WERE UNABLE TO FORM INTO A PLANET DUE TO THE INTERFERENCE OF JUPITER'S MASSIVE GRAVITY.

MARS
THE RED PLANET GETS ITS COLOUR FROM LARGE AMOUNTS OF RUST ON ITS SURFACE.

MERCURY
THE SMALLEST PLANET, MERCURY'S ATMOSPHERE AND OUTER LAYERS HAVE BEEN BLOWN AWAY BY THE SUN'S SOLAR WINDS.

DISCOVERED AFTER MY TIME, **URANUS**, THE COLDEST PLANET, AND **NEPTUNE**, THE WINDIEST PLANET, ORBIT THE SUN EVEN FURTHER OUT THAN SATURN.

BEYOND THEM IS THE **KUIPER BELT**, MOSTLY ASTEROIDS, BUT ALSO CONTAINING MANY DWARF PLANETS, LIKE THE UNFORTUNATE PLUTO (WHICH LOST ITS "PLANET" STATUS AFTER SCIENTISTS DISCOVERED THERE WERE **HUNDREDS** OF SIMILAR OBJECTS OUT THERE!)

AND NOW, GET READY FOR AN INTERVIEW THAT'LL MAKE YOUR **SKIN** CRAWL... AND NOT **JUST** FROM MY OUTRAGEOUS PUNS!

IT'S THE LADY WHO **PRISED OPEN** THE **PRIVATE LIVES** OF ALL SORTS OF CREEPY CRITTERS...

MARIA SIBYLLA MERIAN!

MARIA SIBYLLA MERIAN
ENTOMOLOGIST
1647–1717

MARIA, AFTER LANGUISHING IN OBSCURITY FOR CENTURIES, YOU'VE BEEN RECENTLY REDISCOVERED AS THE FOUNDER OF MODERN **ENTOMOLOGY** (THE STUDY OF BUGS).

PRETTY FREAKY THING TO STUDY IF YOU ASK ME...

WELL, THAT'S WHAT MY FAMILY THOUGHT...

WHY MUST YOU WASTE YOUR TIME ON THOSE HORRIBLE CREATURES!? WHY NOT PAINT SOMETHING **NICE**, LIKE FLOWERS?

SO I WORKED FOR A WHILE PAINTING PRETTY FLORAL PATTERNS FOR PRINTING ON SILK.

BUT YOU JUST COULDN'T RESIST THE **LURE OF BUGS**!?

WELL, YOU SEE, SILK, AND THE SILKWORMS THAT MADE IT, ARE REALLY EXPENSIVE. I THOUGHT I MIGHT BE ABLE TO FIND SOME **OTHER** CATERPILLARS THAT COULD ALSO MAKE SILK.

I DIDN'T, BUT I FOUND SOMETHING EVEN MORE VALUABLE. I WAS THE FIRST PERSON TO REALISE THE TRUE STORY OF THE BUTTERFLY'S LIFE CYCLE!

CATERPILLAR

CHRYSALIS

EGGS

BUTTERFLY

COME ON! DOESN'T **EVERYONE** KNOW THAT!?

NOT SO. AT THIS TIME, THEY WERE STILL JUST PARROTING ARISTOTLE'S BIZARRE THEORIES...

EVERYONE KNOWS THAT INSECTS JUST **MAGICALLY APPEAR** FROM ROTTING FOOD.

RIGHT.

BECAUSE SCIENCE SAYS SO.

SINCE THIS IS CLEARLY THE WORK OF THE **DEVIL**, WE CAN CONCLUDE THAT INSECTS ARE THE DEVIL'S CREATURES.

OF COURSE.

LOGICALLY...

ALSO, FLIES COME FROM MELTING SNOW, AND FROGS ARE BORN OUT OF RAINDROPS...

WOW! SCIENCE IS AMAZING!

YOU PUBLISHED A BOOK BEAUTIFULLY ILLUSTRATING THE **METAMORPHOSIS** OF **50** DIFFERENT CATERPILLARS. IT OVERTURNED ALL THOSE NUTTY THEORIES AND MADE YOU A **SCIENCE SENSATION**!

BUT NOT **EVERYONE** WAS THRILLED WITH YOUR NEW-FOUND FAME...

MY HUSBAND WAS ALSO AN ARTIST. IT DROVE HIM **NUTS** THAT I WAS SO SUCCESSFUL AND HE WASN'T.

MARIA, IT'S **ME** OR THE **BUGS!**

NO CONTEST, REALLY... BEAR IN MIND THOUGH, THIS WAS IN GERMANY, WHERE THEY WERE STILL BURNING WITCHES...

AND I WAS NOW A **SINGLE WOMAN** (SUSPICIOUS) **STUDYING** (ALSO SUSPICIOUS) **INSECTS** (THE DEVIL'S CREATURES). I DECIDED TO MOVE TO HOLLAND.

YOU FOUND A MORE SUPPORTIVE COMMUNITY OF SCIENTISTS IN AMSTERDAM, AND BECAME QUITE RICH DOING SCIENTIFIC ILLUSTRATIONS.

YEAH, BUT FOR **OTHER PEOPLE**...

EXPLORERS WOULD SEND ME THESE AWESOME FREAKY BUGS FROM ALL OVER THE WORLD. BUT THEY WERE ALL DRIED AND STUCK WITH PINS.

HOW CAN YOU TELL WHERE IT LIVES OR WHAT IT EATS IF IT'S STUCK TO A BOARD?

SO YOU DECIDED TO GO AND SEE THEM FOR YOURSELF!

I SOLD ALL MY STUFF, WROTE OUT MY WILL (JUST IN CASE) AND TOOK A SHIP FOR **SURINAME**, A DUTCH COLONY ON THE COAST OF SOUTH AMERICA.

IT WAS QUITE A SHOCK, LET ME TELL YOU! THE STIFLING HEAT, THE CONSTANT RAIN, AND TRAMPING THROUGH THE JUNGLE IN CORSET AND PETTICOATS!

AT HOME, I'D BEEN USED TO STUDYING INSECTS IN GARDENS, MUNCHING ON FLOWERS CONVENIENTLY LOCATED AT EYE-LEVEL.

BUT HERE, ALL THE GOOD BUGS WERE UP IN THE TREE-TOPS **20** STOREYS ABOVE!

AND IF I COULDN'T GET TO THE BUGS, I'D HAVE THEM COME TO ME!

TIMBERRR!

AND WHAT AMAZING CREATURES THEY WERE! MOTHS WITH FOOT-WIDE WINGSPANS!

MASSIVE SPIDERS THAT COULD CATCH AND EAT LIVE BIRDS!

RIVERS OF ANTS!

AND EVERYWHERE, CATERPILLARS! DRAB CATERPILLARS THAT PRODUCED BEAUTIFUL BUTTERFLIES...

AND BEAUTIFUL CATERPILLARS THAT PRODUCED DRAB BUTTERFLIES!

I COULD HAVE STAYED FOREVER! BUT I CAUGHT TROPICAL FEVER AND HAD TO LEAVE AFTER ONLY 2 YEARS!

GUTTED!

YOU CONTINUED WORKING, PUBLISHING A BOOK ILLUSTRATING YOUR **DISGUSTING DISCOVERIES**...

BUGS REALLY AREN'T DISGUSTING! YOU JUST NEED TO GET TO KNOW THEM BETTER! HERE...

OH, THAT'S NICE. HE'S DANCING AROUND WITH DELIGHT...

The CIRCLE of LIFE

MY TRAVELS IN THE JUNGLES OF SURINAME ALLOWED ME TO STUDY MANY WONDERFUL SPECIES OF INSECTS UP CLOSE AND PERSONAL, LIKE THIS AWESOME **ACHILLES MORPHO BUTTERFLY.**

BUTTERFLIES LAY THEIR EGGS ON THE UNDERSIDE OF LEAVES, IN THIS CASE THE LEAVES OF THE WEST INDIAN CHERRY.

WHEN THE EGGS HATCH, THE BUTTERFLY LARVAE, OR **CATERPILLARS,** EMERGE.

MORPHO CATERPILLARS ARE COVERED WITH IRRITATING HAIRS, AND THEY EMIT A FOUL SMELL, TO WARD OFF WOULD-BE PREDATORS.

INSIDE THIS HARD CASE, THE CATERPILLAR'S BODY BREAKS DOWN INTO A SORT OF GROSS SOUP, BEFORE BEING RE-FORMED AS A BUTTERFLY.

THEY EAT AND GROW LIKE CRAZY, SHEDDING THEIR SKIN **5** TIMES BEFORE THEY REACH THEIR MAXIMUM SIZE.

ONCE THEY REACH FULL SIZE, THEY ENTER THE MOST INCREDIBLE PART OF THE WHOLE AMAZING LIFE-CYCLE: THE CHRYSALIS!

THE MORPHO CRYSALIS GIVES OFF AN UNBEARABLE ULTRASONIC SCREECH IF TOUCHED, SO IT STILL HAS A DEFENSE AGAINST PREDATORS.

THE ADULT MORPHO ONLY LIVES FOR **2-3 WEEKS**. WHICH IS ACTUALLY PRETTY GOOD GOING, COMPARED WITH THE **SMALL COPPER** BUTTERFLY WHICH ONLY GETS A FEW **DAYS**!

THEN IT'S OFF TO FIND A MATE AND LAY SOME MORE EGGS, COMPLETING THE WONDERFUL **CIRCLE OF LIFE**.

WHEN THE ADULT BUTTERFLY EMERGES, ITS WINGS ARE SOFT AND FLOPPY. IT PUMPS BLOOD INTO THEM TO MAKE THEM STIFF ENOUGH TO FLY WITH.

MY NEXT GUEST IS OFTEN CALLED THE **MOST IMPORTANT SCIENTIST OF ALL TIME!** WHICH IS PRETTY BIG TALK, BUT THEN THIS GUY HAS SOME PRETTY BIG ACHIEVEMENTS.

PLEASE WELCOME THE **FRUIT-FIXATED FOUNTAINHEAD** OF NATURAL PHILOSOPHY...

SIR **ISAAC NEWTON!**

ISAAC NEWTON
NATURAL PHILOSOPHER
1642–1727

SIR ISAAC, YOU FAMOUSLY FIGURED OUT YOUR THEORY OF HOW GRAVITY WORKS BY WATCHING AN APPLE FALLING FROM A TREE...

-CHORTLE- WELL, ADAM, I THINK YOU MIGHT FIND THAT IT'S NOT **QUITE** AS SIMPLE AS ALL THAT...

IT WAS MY **DEEP STUDY** OF THE GREATEST MATHEMATICIANS AND SCIENTISTS (BEFORE **ME,** THAT IS) THAT ALLOWED ME TO REACH MY **BRILLIANT** CONCLUSIONS...

AS I ALWAYS SAID: IF I SAW FURTHER THAN OTHER MEN, IT WAS BY STANDING ON THE SHOULDERS OF GIANTS...

GUYS LIKE:

EUCLID: INVENTED GEOMETRY

GALILEO*: PROVED THE EARTH GOES AROUND THE SUN

DESCARTES: PROPOSED THE UNIVERSE IS GOVERNED BY MATHEMATICAL LAWS

BUT, GIANTS OR NOT, NONE OF **THEM** HAD REACHED THE **PINNACLE** OF SCIENCE: A COMPLETE THEORY OF HOW THINGS **MOVE!**

TAKE THE FAMOUS APPLE, FOR EXAMPLE. WHEN AN APPLE FALLS FROM A TREE, IT STARTS OFF **NOT MOVING**, AND THEN SPEEDS UP AS IT FALLS...

I HAD TO INVENT A TOTALLY NEW KIND OF MATHS (I BELIEVE YOU NOW CALL IT **CALCULUS**) TO DEAL WITH THINGS THAT KEEP CHANGING, LIKE THE APPLE'S SPEED.

COMBINED WITH CAREFUL **EXPERIMENTS**, TO CHECK I WAS REALLY ON THE RIGHT TRACK, I COULD CONSTRUCT A **MATHEMATICAL MODEL** TO DESCRIBE THE APPLE'S MOTION.

BUT I DIDN'T STOP WITH APPLES! I REALISED THAT **EVERYTHING** EXERTS A GRAVITATIONAL PULL ON EVERYTHING ELSE! AT THE SAME TIME THE EARTH IS PULLING YOU DOWN, **YOU'RE** PULLING IT **UP!**

RAAG!

OF COURSE, YOU'RE SO MUCH SMALLER THAN THE EARTH, YOUR GRAVITY IS COMPLETELY **IGNORABLE**.

AW!

THE PULL OF GRAVITY COMES FROM HOW **BIG** AND ALSO HOW **CLOSE** AN OBJECT IS. SO I COULD USE THOSE NUMBERS TO **PREDICT** THE ORBITS OF THE PLANETS.

I HAD BECOME THE FIRST PERSON IN **HISTORY** TO BE ABLE TO CALCULATE HOW EVERYTHING IN THE UNIVERSE, NO MATTER HOW LARGE OR SMALL, MOVED AND INTERACTED.

LIKE PEEKING INTO THE MIND OF **GOD!**

TODAY WE USE CALCULUS IN EVERYTHING, FROM PLANNING SPACE FLIGHTS, TO STUDYING THE GROWTH OF BACTERIA, TO PREDICTING IF THE STOCK MARKET WILL MAKE MONEY OR NOT, AND IT ALL STARTED WITH YOU!

*SEE PAGE **26**

SO I TAKE IT YOU **PUBLISHED** YOUR AMAZING DISCOVERIES FOR EVERYONE ELSE TO USE IN THEIR OWN SCIENTIFIC INVESTIGATIONS...

WHAT? NO!

AND LET ALL THOSE **HATERS** CRITICISE MY BEAUTIFUL THEORIES?! OR STEAL THEM AND TAKE THE CREDIT FOR THEMSELVES?

THIEVES... HATERS...

EVERYWHERE...

MUTTER MUTTER...

I ONLY SHARED THE **BARE MINIMUM** TO GET A PROFESSORSHIP, SO I COULD CONTINUE MY RESEARCH.

BUT EVEN **THAT** PROVED TOO MUCH FOR YOU. PEOPLE JUST ASKING **QUESTIONS** ABOUT YOUR NEW THEORIES WAS ENOUGH TO SEND YOU INTO A 6-YEAR-LONG **SULK!**

YOU REFUSED TO SPEAK TO ANYONE OR EVEN ANSWER LETTERS, UNTIL **EDMUND HALLEY** (OF HALLEY'S COMET FAME) COAXED YOU OUT OF IT.

OH, COME ON, ISAAC! EVERYONE THINKS YOU'RE GREAT!

HE CONVINCED YOU TO WRITE IT ALL DOWN IN WHAT BECAME POSSIBLY THE MOST IMPORTANT BOOK IN THE HISTORY OF SCIENCE: THE **PHILOSOPHIÆ NATURALIS PRINCIPIA MATHEMATICA!**

THE SCIENCE COMMUNITY, THEIR MINDS WELL AND TRULY BLOWN, **SHOWERED** YOU WITH HONOURS AND RECOGNITION.

CAUSING YOU TO DESCEND INTO **ANOTHER** PARANOID FRENZY.

I know you're all out to get me...

WHAT **IS** IT WITH YOU?

HEY! I WROTE EVERYONE LETTERS OF APOLOGY.

EXCEPT, UH... GERMAN MATHEMATICIAN **GOTTFRIED LEIBNIZ**

THAT DIRTY CHEAT! HE STOLE MY CALCULUS AND CLAIMED **HE** INVENTED IT!

BUT DON'T WORRY. I USED MY FAME AND RECOGNITION TO GET EVERYONE TO AGREE THAT HE WAS A **THIEF!**

EXCEPT, WELL, HE **DOES** SEEM TO HAVE INVENTED IT SEPARATELY, AND HIS SYSTEM **IS**, ER... A BIT BETTER, SO... THAT'S THE ONE WE USE... TODAY...?

ARGH! CURSE YOU GOTTFRIED LEIBNIZ!

ANYWAY, WHAT DO **YOU** CARE? YOU **GAVE UP** ON SCIENCE AFTER THAT TO WORK ON YOUR NEW JOB AS MASTER OF THE MINT!

HUFF! HUFF!

SO I GUESS YOU COULD SAY YOU WENT FROM MINTY FRESH SCIENCE TO MINTY FRESH **BREATH!**

NOT **THAT** KIND OF MINT!

GEEZ. THIS IS THE **ROYAL MINT**, WHERE ALL THE MONEY IS MADE.

OBVIOUSLY.

IT WAS SUPPOSED TO BE A **CEREMONIAL** POSITION. YOU KNOW: "HERE, HAVE A CUSHY JOB SO YOU CAN KEEP DOING SCIENCE ON THE SIDE..."

BUT I ACTUALLY FOUND IT FASCINATING! FOR EXAMPLE, THERE WAS A BIG PROBLEM AT THE TIME WITH PEOPLE CUTTING BITS OFF THE EDGES OF COINS TO SELL THE SILVER.

SO I INVENTED THE LITTLE GROVES ON THE EDGE OF COINS SO IF YOU CLIP BITS OFF, YOU'LL GET CAUGHT. YOUR COINS STILL USE MY SYSTEM TODAY.

BAH!

SO THERE YOU GO: **ISSAC NEWTON**. DISCOVERER OF THE LAWS OF THE UNIVERSE AND INVENTOR OF THE LITTLE GROOVES ON COINS.

JUST SO LONG AS I GET THE CREDIT...

I'M **GIVING** YOU THE CREDIT.

WELL, GOOD. YOU'D BETTER.

LAYING DOWN THE LAWS

SO YOU'VE JUST MET **SIR ISAAC NEWTON**, WHOSE DISCOVERIES HERALDED THE **SCIENTIFIC REVOLUTION!** NOW IT'S TIME FOR SIR ISAAC TO **LAY DOWN THE LAWS!**

THE **LAWS OF MOTION** THAT IS!

DON'T FORGET, IT WAS THESE LAWS, COMBINED WITH MY THEORIES ON GRAVITY AND MY NEW MATHEMATICS, THAT **BLEW** THE COLLECTIVE **MINDS** OF THE SCIENTIFIC COMMUNITY AND CHANGED THE WORLD FOREVER.

ARE YOU **READY** FOR THAT SORT OF KNOWLEDGE?

DO YOU REALLY THINK YOU CAN HANDLE...

NEWTON'S THREE LAWS OF MOTION?!

❧ Law 1 ❧
NOTHING **STARTS** OR **STOPS** MOVING, OR **CHANGES SPEED**, UNLESS SOMETHING ELSE PUSHES IT.

❧ Law 2 ❧
HOW **FAST** SOMETHING CHANGES SPEED DEPENDS ON HOW **HEAVY** IT IS, AND HOW **HARD** YOU PUSH IT.

❧ Law 3 ❧
IF SOMETHING PUSHES IN ONE DIRECTION, THERE WILL ALWAYS BE AN **EQUAL** PUSH IN THE **OPPOSITE DIRECTION**.

OK, OK, HOLD ON. THAT DOESN'T MAKE ANY SENSE.

HM. DIDN'T **THINK** YOU COULD HANDLE IT...

NO, LOOK, YOU SAID NOTHING **STOPS** MOVING UNLESS SOMETHING PUSHES IT...

BUT EVERYTHING STOPS MOVING **EVENTUALLY**. EVEN IF IT DOESN'T HIT AN OBSTACLE, IT'LL JUST SLOW DOWN AND STOP ON ITS OWN.

AHA! YES, BUT ONLY HERE ON EARTH!

IN SPACE THERE'S NOTHING TO BUMP AGAINST, NOT EVEN **AIR**, SO IF YOU PUSH SOMETHING, IT JUST KEEPS GOING. FOREVER.

THANK GOODNESS I HAVE THIS SAFETY LINE...

BUT ON EARTH, THINGS SLOW DOWN DUE TO **FRICTION**, WHICH IS OTHER STUFF (LIKE THE GROUND, OR THE AIR) **RUBBING** THE MOVING OBJECT, AND THAT'S WHAT PUSHES AGAINST IT.

FRICTION

WHICH IS WHY, IF YOU WANT TO ENJOY MY THREE LAWS IN THEIR **PUREST** FORM, YOU NEED TO BUILD SOMETHING LIKE...

A Home-made Hovercraft!

43

WHAT YOU WILL NEED:

1. AN OLD CD (MAKE SURE NO ONE NEEDS IT).

HAS ANYONE SEEN MY SPICE GIRLS GREATEST HITS?

2. A BALLOON (MAKE SURE NO ONE NEEDS IT EITHER).

UM...

3. STICKY TAPE (DON'T GET STUCK!)

MUUUUM!

4. THE POP-UP CAP FROM AN EMPTY DRINK OR WASHING-UP LIQUID BOTTLE (MAKE SURE IT'S PROPERLY WASHED OUT).

ARE YOU DONE WITH THAT?

HOW TO MAKE IT:

1. USE TAPE TO STICK THE BOTTLE CAP ONTO THE CD. BE SURE TO TAPE ALL THE WAY AROUND TO MAKE AN AIRTIGHT SEAL.

VERY IMPORTANT!

2. STRETCH THE BALLOON NECK OVER THE BOTTLE CAP, MAKING SURE THAT IT'S SECURE AND FITS TIGHTLY.

3. POP OPEN THE CAP, BLOW UP THE BALLOON (THROUGH THE CD HOLE) AND THEN POP THE CAP CLOSED TO KEEP THE AIR IN.

4. PLACE ON A FLAT SURFACE, THEN CAREFULLY OPEN THE CAP A LITTLE BIT. AIR WILL BLOW OUT AND HOVER THE HOVERCRAFT!

POP!

LAW **1**: IT KEEPS MOVING FOREVER (OR UNTIL THE AIR RUNS OUT, WHICHEVER HAPPENS FIRST.)

(THE AIR STOPS THE HOVERCRAFT TOUCHING THE GROUND — REDUCING **FRICTION** ALMOST TO NOTHING!)

LAW **2**: HOW FAST IT GOES DEPENDS ON HOW HARD YOU PUSH IT.

LAW **3**: AS THE AIR PUSHES DOWN IT LIFTS THE HOVERCRAFT UP.

CHALLENGE YOUR FRIENDS TO A **HOVERCRAFT PENALTY SHOOT-OUT!**

AND NOW, A TRUE **SUPERHERO** SCIENTIST. MEET ONE OF HISTORY'S GREATEST **LIFESAVERS**, THE MAN WHO RID THE WORLD OF THE KILLER VIRUS **SMALLPOX**!

IT'S THE MASTER OF MEDICINE, THE **DESTROYER OF DISEASE**, THE INVENTOR OF IMMUNISATION...

EDWARD JENNER!

EDWARD JENNER
PHYSICIAN
1749-1823

JENNER, YOU DEVOTED YOUR LIFE TO THE STRUGGLE AGAINST SMALLPOX. NOW, I KNOW IT'S A DEADLY DISEASE, BUT IT SOUNDS A BIT... **SMALL**... WOULD YOU NOT HAVE BEEN BETTER FIGHTING... **BIGPOX** OR SOMETHING?

DON'T LET THE NAME FOOL YOU. SMALLPOX WAS A **BIG** KILLER, WHICH CLAIMED **MILLIONS** OF LIVES.

THE NAME COMES FROM SMALL, PUS-FILLED BOILS THAT COVER THE SUFFERER'S BODY FROM HEAD TO TOE.

IF YOU CAUGHT IT, YOU'D MOST LIKELY BE DEAD IN DAYS. BUT EVEN THE SURVIVORS WOULD BE HORRIBLY **DISFIGURED.**

THE RICH TOOK TO WEARING **POWDER** AND **BEAUTY MARKS** TO TRY AND COVER UP THEIR SCARS.

AND IT WAS BASICALLY **UNTREATABLE?**

OH, THERE WAS A TREATMENT: "VARIOLATION"

ALTHOUGH, YOU COULD SAY THE TREATMENT WAS NEARLY AS BAD AS THE DISEASE ITSELF!

THE THING THAT EVERYONE KNEW ABOUT SMALLPOX WAS, ONCE YOU'D HAD IT, YOU COULDN'T CATCH IT AGAIN.

SO WHY NOT JUST GET IT OVER WITH!? WITH VARIOLATION, THE VIRUS WAS DELIVERED TO YOUR DOORSTEP IN THE FORM OF **INFECTIOUS SMALLPOX SCABS.**

KIDS WOULD GET INFECTED WITH THE STUFF AND THEN LOCKED UP IN A BARN FOR DAYS. WHEN YOU CAME OUT, YOU'D BE **IMMUNE.** THAT IS, **IF** YOU CAME OUT AT ALL...

I'VE NEVER FORGOTTEN: THE DARKNESS, THE PAIN, THE STENCH OF DEATH...

WHOA!? THAT'S **YOU!?**

YES, I WAS ONE OF THE LUCKY ONES — I SURVIVED.

I STUDIED MEDICINE, HOPING THAT I COULD SAVE OTHERS FROM SUFFERING AS I HAD.

BUT SMALLPOX KEPT ON KILLING, AND I HAD NO IDEA EVEN WHERE TO **BEGIN** THE SEARCH FOR A CURE.

47

I WAS WORKING AS A COUNTRY DOCTOR, AND I'D BASICALLY GIVEN UP MY QUEST, WHEN A MASSIVE **CLUE** FELL IN MY LAP.

THE LOCAL PEOPLE TALKED ABOUT HOW **MILKMAIDS** ALWAYS HAD BEAUTIFUL SKIN BECAUSE THEY NEVER GOT SMALLPOX.

BUT THE MILKMAIDS **DID** GET A VERY MILD INFECTION CALLED **COWPOX.**

MILD HEADACHE

SPOTS ON HANDS

OH. MY. **DAYS.**

THAT'S **IT!** COWPOX IS PROTECTING THEM!

AND COWPOX IS TOTALLY HARMLESS! NO ONE WOULD EVER HAVE TO GO THROUGH THE HORROR OF VARIOLATION AGAIN!

NOW I JUST NEEDED TO FIND A GUINEA-PIG TO TEST IT OUT ON. SOMEONE WHO HAD NEVER HAD EITHER DISEASE...

HMM...

JAMES PHIPPS. THE GARDENER'S SON. AGE **8.**

MAN! I CAN'T EVEN **IMAGINE** WHAT YOU SAID TO CONVINCE HIS PARENTS...

I JUST EXPLAINED THAT I WANTED TO CUT HIS ARM OPEN AND PUSH LITTLE BITS OF SOME MILKMAID'S **COWPOX SCABS** INTO THE WOUND...

AND THEN DO THE SAME THING, BUT THIS TIME WITH **LIVE, POTENTIALLY DEADLY** SMALLPOX SCABS, TO SEE IF THE TREATMENT WORKED.

SO BASICALLY, YOU COULD'VE KILLED HIM.

BUT I DIDN'T! HE DIDN'T EVEN GET SICK!

YOU COULD PUMP DISGUSTING SMALLPOX MATTER INTO HIM **ALL DAY LONG** AND IT WOULDN'T BOTHER HIM IN THE **SLIGHTEST!**

I CALLED MY NEW TREATMENT VACCINATION! FROM "VACCA", THE LATIN FOR COW.

RIGHT. I KNEW THAT...

I COULDN'T WAIT TO SHARE MY AMAZING DISCOVERY WITH THE WORLD!

BUT THE WORLD WASN'T QUITE READY FOR IT...

DESPITE BEING OFFERED FOR FREE, LOTS OF PEOPLE WERE AFRAID OF THE NEW TREATMENT.

FROM COWS!? THAT'S UNNATURAL!

FORTUNATELY, FACTS OVERTOOK FEARS, WHEN PEOPLE STARTED TO SEE HOW MANY LIVES IT SAVED.

MISSIONS WERE SENT OUT ALL OVER THE WORLD TO SPREAD THE VACCINE.

OW!
OW!
OW!
OW!
OW!
OW!

IT TOOK OVER 100 YEARS, BUT EVENTUALLY SMALLPOX WAS COMPLETELY ERADICATED FROM THE WORLD. IT'S THE ONLY DISEASE EVER TO SIMPLY CEASE TO EXIST.

PLUS WE USE THE MODERN VERSION OF YOUR TREATMENT TO PROTECT AGAINST ALL SORTS OF DISEASES.

IN FACT, THROUGH YOUR DISCOVERY, YOU MAY HAVE SAVED MORE LIVES THAN ANYONE ELSE IN HISTORY!

AND IT ALL STARTED FROM A HUMBLE COW...

NOW THAT'S WHAT I CALL A MOO-VING STORY!

-GROAN!-

WHAT AN UDDERLY DREADFUL PUN!

VACCINATION STATIONS

I DEVELOPED MY SMALLPOX VACCINE THROUGH **OBSERVATION** AND **CAREFUL GUESSWORK**, BUT SCIENCE CAN NOW ACTUALLY **EXPLAIN** HOW THE IMMUNE SYSTEM WORKS.

WHICH IS PRETTY AWESOME, FRANKLY.

HERE'S WHAT HAPPENS:

YOUR FIRST LINE OF DEFENCE IS YOUR **WHITE BLOOD CELLS.**

ON FIRST CONTACT WITH **ALIEN INVADERS**, THESE GENERAL-PURPOSE GERM-KILLERS RUSH TO THE ATTACK, FIGHTING THE ENEMY AS BEST THEY CAN.

THEN IT'S TIME TO CALL IN THE IMMUNE SYSTEM'S **ELITE NINJA WARRIORS...**

THE **KILLER T** CELLS (YES, THEY'RE AS COOL AS THEY SOUND).

THEY MULTIPLY LIKE CRAZY, HUNT DOWN THE INTRUDERS, LOCK ONTO THEIR ANTIGENS AND SPRAY THOSE SUCKERS WITH GERM-DESTROYING **TOXIC CHEMICALS.**

THOSE GERMS ARE **TOAST!**

THEY ARE DEDICATED GERM-KILLERS, AND THEY'RE SPECIALLY DESIGNED TO LOCK ONTO THE INVADER'S **ANTIGENS.**

IF YOUR KILLER T CELLS ARE PREPARED, THEY WILL OFTEN FIGHT OFF AN INFECTION BEFORE YOU EVEN NOTICE YOU'RE SICK. THIS IS CALLED BEING **IMMUNE.**

THE TROUBLE IS, THE **FIRST** TIME YOU MEET A NEW INVADER, THE WHOLE PROCESS CAN TAKE SEVERAL WEEKS.

AND THAT'S IF YOU'RE LUCKY! SERIOUS DISEASES, LIKE SMALLPOX, MIGHT **KILL** YOU BEFORE YOUR IMMUNE SYSTEM CAN GET UP TO SPEED.

PRETTY SWEET!

DURING WHICH TIME YOU'RE STILL GONNA FEEL SICK.

THIS GUEST IS QUITE LITERALLY **GROUND-BREAKING.** SHE DEFIED ALL THE ODDS TO BECOME ONE OF THE FOREMOST FOUNDERS OF THE SCIENCE OF **PALAEONTOLOGY.**

PLEASE GIVE A **PREHISTORIC** WELCOME TO PHENOMENALLY FEARLESS FOSSIL-FINDER...

MARY ANNING!

MARY ANNING
PALAEONTOLOGIST
1799-1847

MARY, TODAY YOU'RE KNOWN AS A **SCIENCE SUPERHERO** FOR YOUR ROLE IN THE RECONSTRUCTION OF THE **DEEP PAST.** YOU EVEN HAVE YOUR OWN SUPERHERO **ORIGIN STORY...**

...UH, SURE. YOU COULD PUT IT THAT WAY. WHEN I WAS A BABY, SOME NEIGHBOURS TOOK ME OUT FOR THE DAY...

WHEN **LIGHTNING** HIT THE TREE WE WERE UNDER!

52

THEY WERE ALL **KILLED INSTANTLY**, BUT I WAS NOT ONLY **UNHARMED**, BUT SUPPOSEDLY I BECAME NOTICEABLY MORE ALERT, INTELLIGENT AND CURIOUS.

SO BASICALLY — **LIGHTNING-POWERED SUPER-BRAIN!**

I THINK YOU'RE TAKING THIS A BIT TOO LITERALLY...

BUT INSTEAD OF BECOMING A REANIMATED DINOSAUR-RIDING **SUPER-VILLAIN** (WHICH WOULD HAVE BEEN **MY** PREFERRED OPTION) YOU CHOSE TO USE YOUR **UNCANNY ABILITIES** FOR **GOOD.**

BY ADVANCING THE CAUSE OF SCIENCE! BUT WHAT MADE YOU CHOOSE **FOSSILS** (RATHER THAN, SAY, SHOOTING GIANT LIGHTNING BOLTS OUT OF YOUR FINGERTIPS)?

WELL, APART FROM FOSSILS BEING, Y'KNOW, **REAL**...

PSHAW.

IT ACTUALLY STARTED AS A WAY TO MAKE SOME **CASH**...

THE CLIFFS AROUND MY CHILDHOOD HOME IN **DORSET** HAD ONCE BEEN A PREHISTORIC SEABED.

WHICH MEANT THEY WERE CHOCK-A-BLOCK WITH THE FOSSILS OF ANIMALS THAT HAD DIED AND BEEN BURIED IN THAT ANCIENT SEA MUD.

UNTIL YOU UNCOVERED THEM USING YOUR X-RAY...

OH GEEZ, ENOUGH ALREADY. THE CLIFFS WERE JUST REALLY UNSTABLE...

LANDSLIDES HAPPENED ALL THE TIME, REVEALING FRESH ROCKS THAT JUST **MIGHT** HAVE A FANTASTIC FOSSIL IN THEM.

IT WAS MY **DAD**, WHO HAD THE IDEA OF GATHERING FOSSILS UNCOVERED AFTER A BIG STORM AND SELLING THEM TO TOURISTS!

BUT HE DIED WHEN I WAS JUST A LITTLE GIRL. MY FAMILY HAD NO OTHER WAY TO MAKE MONEY. SO, NO MATTER THE HEARTBREAK, OR THE DANGER, I HAD **NO CHOICE** BUT TO TAKE TO THE CLIFFS AGAIN.

ALTHOUGH IN FAIRNESS, HOW COULD I DO ANYTHING ELSE? ONCE YOU'VE CRACKED OPEN A ROCK AND FOUND SOME AMAZING CREATURE NO HUMAN EYES HAVE SEEN BEFORE, IT'S HARD TO GO BACK...

YOUR FOSSIL FINDS WERE A **SENSATION**, THRILLING MUSEUM-GOERS AND REVEALING A HITHERTO UNKNOWN PREHISTORIC WORLD INHABITED BY LONG-EXTINCT **LIZARD LEVIATHANS**.

CREATURES LIKE THE DOLPHIN-LIKE **ICHTHYOSAUR**, THE NESSIE-LIKE **PLESIOSAUR**, OR THE TERRIFYING BAT-WINGED **DIMORPHODON**; JUST SOME OF THE STAGGERING SPECIES YOU STUMBLED UPON.

WHICH WAS PRETTY FRUSTRATING, ACTUALLY. MY FOSSILS WERE MORE FAMOUS THAN **I** WAS!

THE MUSEUMS, AND THE SCIENTISTS, WERE ALL QUITE HAPPY TO IGNORE ME.

WHOA!

LOOK AT THOSE TEETH!

UM...

BUT I WASN'T JUST A **HIRED FOSSIL-DIGGER**. I'D STUDIED ALL THE SCIENTIFIC RESEARCH OF THE DAY (BY **MYSELF** I MIGHT ADD, SINCE I WAS TOO POOR TO GO TO UNIVERSITY).

I'D EVEN DONE MY OWN ANATOMICAL **DISSECTIONS** TO BETTER UNDERSTAND HOW FOSSIL ANIMALS' BONES FITTED TOGETHER.

AND THE SCIENTISTS WHO **BOUGHT** MY FOSSILS WERE HAPPY ENOUGH TO PICK MY BRAINS ON THE SUBJECT...

AND THEN PUBLISH THE RESULTS AS THEIR OWN WORK!

My Awesome Theory, by A. Genius

SHOCKING! BUT WHY NOT JUST PUBLISH YOUR THEORIES YOURSELF?

WELL, A SERIOUS SCIENTIFIC PAPER COULD ONLY BE PUBLISHED THROUGH THE **GEOLOGICAL SOCIETY**...

The JURASSIC WORLD

LET'S HEAR IT FOR DINOSAUR-DIGGER MARY ANNING...

UM...THE FOSSILS I FOUND ARE NOT **TECHNICALLY** DINOSAURS...

UH...THEY'RE BIG EXTINCT REPTILES, RIGHT?

SURE. BUT PALAEONTOLOGISTS USE THE SHAPE OF **BONES** TO GROUP THOSE EXTINCT REPTILES INTO ORERS, JUST **ONE** OF WHICH IS THE DINOSAURS.

DURIA ANTIQUIOR, A PAINTING NOT UNLIKE THIS ONE, WAS BASED ON MY FOSSILS. IT WAS THE FIRST EVER EXAMPLE OF **PALEO-ART**, WHICH USES SCIENTISTS' FINDINGS TO BRING THE WORLD OF LONG-EXTINCT ANIMALS BACK TO LIFE.

PLESIOSAURUS

PLESIOSAURS WERE SLOW-SWIMMING SEA MONSTERS, WHICH PROBABLY SNAPPED UNSUSPECTING FISH OR SQUID NEAR THE WATER'S SURFACE.

NOT, UNFORTUNATELY, SNAPPING DIMORPHODON OUT OF THE SKY. BUT WE DIDN'T KNOW THAT AT THE TIME.

WHEN I FOUND MY FIRST SPECIMEN, SCIENTISTS WERE WEIRDED OUT BY ITS LONG NECK. IT WAS SO UTTERLY UNLIKE ANYTHING THEY'D SEEN BEFORE, THEY WERE CONVINCED IT WAS A FAKE!

HA! SOON SHOWED THEM!

CHARLES, YOU WERE A PROFESSOR OF MATHEMATICS. THAT MUST'VE BEEN A DIFFICULT JOB BEFORE THE INVENTION OF CALCULATORS!

IT WAS! I HAD TO DO LOTS OF REALLY HARD SUMS BY HAND! ONE THING WE HAD TO SAVE TIME WAS **TABLES** – BIG LISTS OF ALL THE POSSIBLE ANSWERS TO HARD SUMS.

TROUBLE WAS, ALL THE CALCULATIONS WERE BEING DONE BY **HAND**, AND PEOPLE MAKE MISTAKES.

NOW... CARRY THE ONE...

WELL, THAT'S JUST INFURIATING! I LOST **DAYS** OF WORK EACH TIME I HAD TO GO BACK AND REDO ALL MY CALCULATIONS.

AND IT WASN'T JUST MATHEMATICIANS! **SAILORS** USED THESE DODGY TABLES TO NAVIGATE WITH.

NOW... CARRY THE ONE...

I REALISED, IF YOU COULD GET A **MACHINE** TO DO THE CALCULATIONS, IT WOULD NEVER BE WRONG!

SO I SET OUT TO DESIGN ONE...

AN INTRICATE SERIES OF COGS WOULD STORE THE NUMBERS.

EACH ONE WOULD TURN INTO POSITION TO MAKE THE CALCULATION.

IT WOULD WORK BY CALCULATING THE **DIFFERENCE** BETWEEN THE NUMBERS, SO I CALLED IT THE **DIFFERENCE ENGINE.**

(LIKE IN YOUR **3** TIMES TABLES: THE DIFFERENCE BETWEEN THE NUMBERS IS ALWAYS **3**.)

SORT OF LIKE A GIANT, STEAM-POWERED CALCULATOR.

EXACTLY!

HE'S NOT AS DUMB AS HE LOOKS...

I BUILT A LITTLE MODEL TO DEMONSTRATE THE PRINCIPLE.

THIS IS INCREDIBLE!

HERE! HAVE LOTS OF MONEY!

GOVERNMENT

IT WOULD'VE BEEN INCREDIBLE! **15** TONS OF BRASS AND STEEL, **125,000** MOVING PARTS CAPABLE OF CALCULATING HARD SUMS TO **31** DECIMAL PLACES.

SO ACCURATE...

CHUGGA CHUGGA CHUGGA CHUGGA CHUGGA

WOULD'VE BEEN... MEANING IT WAS NEVER BUILT.

I WAS **FOILED** AT EVERY TURN!

FIRST, BY THE PATHETICALLY INACCURATE MANUFACTURING STANDARDS OF THE TIME...

NOT **GOOD** ENOUGH!

WELL, **YOU** TRY DOING IT!

I SPENT AGES TRAVELLING THE COUNTRY, STUDYING MANUFACTURING PROCESSES AND IMPROVING THE QUALITY OF BRITISH ENGINEERING AS A RESULT.

BUT EVERY TIME YOU THOUGHT OF AN IMPROVEMENT YOU WENT BACK AND STARTED EVERYTHING OVER.

RIGHT. BECAUSE IT HAD TO BE **PERFECT!**

THE GOVERNMENT GOT FED UP AND **CUT OFF** YOUR FUNDING.

GUYS! JUST A FEW MORE MONTHS!

YOU SAID THAT LIKE THREE **YEARS** AGO.

MAYBE TRY INVENTING A MACHINE TO CALCULATE WHEN YOU'LL BE **FINISHED!**

HA HA HA HA HA HA

BUT ALL OF THESE WERE JUST MINOR ANNOYANCES, TRIVIAL SETBACKS, COMPARED TO THE **REAL** THORN IN MY SIDE, THE **BANE OF MY EXISTENCE...**

MUSICIANS!

MUSICIANS?

OH, LORD... HERE WE GO...

AWFUL ACCORDIONISTS! ORGAN GRINDERS! GERMAN OOMPAH BANDS! **HURDY-GURDY PLAYERS!**

HAVE YOU EVER **HEARD** A **HURDY-GURDY**!?

HORRENDOUS!

IMAGINE! I'VE JUST GOT INTO A PARTICULARLY DIFFICULT PIECE OF WORK, DESIGNING THE OPERATION OF A MACHINE NO ONE HAS EVER EVEN **IMAGINED**, LET ALONE BUILT...

WHEN IN THROUGH THE WINDOW COMES THIS DREADFUL NOISE OF ABSOLUTE **MAXIMUM IRRITATINGNESS!**

COULDN'T YOU JUST, Y'KNOW, TUNE IT OUT?

NO! MAYBE WITH SOMETHING LIKE TRAFFIC NOISE YOU CAN GET USED TO IT, BUT THIS IS NOISE **DESIGNED** TO BE UN-IGNORABLE!

OF COURSE I RAN OUTSIDE TO REMONSTRATE WITH THEM, BUT THEY JUST MOVED A FEW DOORS DOWN AND STARTED AGAIN!

IN VAIN DID I APPEAL TO THE POLICE, THE MAGISTRATES AND THE GOVERNMENT.

I WROTE MANY LENGTHY AND IMPASSIONED PLEAS TO THE NEWSPAPERS...

Dear Sir,
it is with _great_ indignation that I must take up my pen with regard to the gr... menace stalk...

THE ONLY RESULT OF WHICH WAS THAT **ALL** THE STREET MUSICIANS IN LONDON TOOK TO COMING TO PLAY OUTSIDE MY WINDOW AS **LOUDLY** AND AS **BADLY** AS THEY COULD.

YOU MUST ADMIT, YOU **DID** HAVE A SPECIAL TALENT FOR GETTING PEOPLE'S BACKS UP...

THEY WERE CLEARLY ALL STUNTED IMBECILES, JEALOUS OF MY VASTLY SUPERIOR INTELLIGENCE!

YOU SEE WHAT I'M TALKING ABOUT...

AND ALL THE WHILE YOUR DIFFERENCE ENGINE WAS LANGUISHING HALF-FINISHED...

BUT THEN I HAD A **NEW** IDEA!

I STARTED THINKING, IF I COULD BUILD A MACHINE TO DO **ONE** KIND OF CALCULATION...

BUT YOU DIDN'T...

NO, BUT I **COULD HAVE**. YOU DON'T GET TO BE THIS CLEVER WITHOUT BEING ABLE TO VISUALISE YOUR INVENTIONS BEFORE THEY'RE BUILT. I **KNEW** IT WORKED!

ANYWAY, THAT'S NOT THE POINT — I HAD THIS NEW IDEA — INSTEAD OF THE DIFFERENCE ENGINE, I WOULD BUILD THE **ANALYTIC ENGINE**!

WHAT'S THE DIFFERENCE?

WELL, THE DIFFERENCE ENGINE COULD ONLY DO ONE TYPE OF CALCULATION. THE ANALYTIC MACHINE COULD BE **PROGRAMMED** TO DO **ANY TYPE** OF CALCULATION AT ALL!

AT ITS HEART WAS AN ADVANCED VERSION OF THE DIFFERENCE ENGINE, CAPABLE OF MANY MORE TYPES OF CALCULATIONS...

CHKKA CHKKA CHKKA

"THE MILL"

CHKKA CHKKA

IT HAD A VAST MEMORY BANK, STORING NUMBERS FOR FUTURE USE.

"THE STORE"

INSTRUCTIONS COULD BE FED IN ON CARDS WITH HOLES PUNCHED IN THEM.

WARRRRR

RESULTS COULD BE PRINTED BY AN AUTOMATIC TYPEWRITER.

WAIT, WAIT. IT STILL SOUNDS LIKE A CALCULATOR. MAYBE ONE OF THOSE FANCY ONES WITH ALL THE EXTRA BUTTONS...

WELL, THAT'S WHERE **ADA** COMES IN...

ABOUT TIME! I BECAME THE HIGH PRIESTESS OF CHARLES'S AMAZING MACHINE, USING THE MAGIC OF MATHS TO FIGHT THE EVILS OF **POETRY**.

HOLD ON. WHAT!?

MY FATHER WAS **LORD BYRON**, THE FAMOUS POET.

IN A LIFE FILLED WITH WILD AND DISSOLUTE SCANDALS, ONE OF HIS WORST WAS DESERTING MY MOTHER AND ME WHEN I WAS JUST **ONE MONTH** OLD.

SO, ALTHOUGH I NEVER KNEW HIM, I HEARD PLENTY ABOUT HIM, AND ESPECIALLY HOW THE **EVIL SPIRIT OF POETRY** HAD DRIVEN HIM MAD.

SINCE I **WAS** HIS CHILD, MOTHER FEARED THAT I MIGHT HAVE INHERITED HIS EVIL GIFTS.

SO SHE RESOLVED TO COMBAT THE PERNICIOUS INFLUENCE OF POETRY WITH ITS **PERFECT OPPOSITE**...

MATHEMATICS!

OF COURSE, THERE WERE NO SCHOOLS FOR GIRLS BACK THEN. THEY BELIEVED THE STRAIN OF LEARNING WOULD BE TOO MUCH FOR OUR DELICATE MINDS.

BUT MOTHER AND I WERE **NOBILITY**. SO WE COULD DO WHAT WE LIKED.

MOTHER ARRANGED FOR ME TO MEET, AND TAKE LESSONS FROM, ALL THE GREAT MATHEMATICIANS OF THE DAY.

AND THAT WAS HOW WE MET, AT ONE OF THE **INTELLECTUAL SOIREES** AT CHARLES'S HOUSE...

A CHANCE FOR THE COUNTRY'S **GREAT MINDS** TO MEET AND EXCHANGE VIEWS.

AND SHOW OFF HOW **SMART** THEY WERE...

HRM. WELL, YES, A HEALTHY REGARD FOR ONE'S OWN INTELLECT IS NO BAD THING...

ANYWAY, THAT WAS WHERE I FIRST SAW THE PLANS FOR THE ANALYTIC ENGINE.

BAH! NO ONE IS **CAPABLE** OF UNDERSTANDING MY VISIONARY GENIUS...

ASTOUNDING! THE MECHANICAL REPRESENTATION OF ABSTRACT MATHEMATICS WILL ALLOW FASTER AND DEEPER ANALYSIS THAN HERETOFOR IMAGINABLE!

YES! EXACTLY!

INCREDIBLE. IN THIS **17** YEAR-OLD-GIRL I HAD, AT LAST, FOUND MY PROPHET!

AND SO BEGAN AN EXTRAORDINARY FRIENDSHIP, CONDUCTED ALMOST ENTIRELY BY LETTER; A VAST CORRESPONDENCE OF SUGGESTIONS, PLANS, AND IMPROVEMENTS FOR THE ANALYTIC ENGINE.

BUT VERY QUICKLY YOU CAME TO THE REALISATION THAT THE MACHINE WAS MORE IMPORTANT THAN EVEN **CHARLES** BELIEVED.

AND THAT'S SAYING SOMETHING!

YES, WELL, YOU SEE, HERE WE HAD A MACHINE THAT COULD STORE AND PROCESS MUCH MORE THAN NUMBERS...

IF YOU ASSIGN EACH LETTER OF THE ALPHABET A NUMBER — A=**1**, B=**2** AND SO ON... THEN YOU COULD ALSO ENTER **LETTERS**.

AND IT COULD BE **PROGRAMMED**, SO YOU COULD TELL IT WHAT TO **DO** WITH THOSE LETTERS.

YOU COULD USE IT TO CRACK SECRET CODES, YOU COULD SEARCH FOR INFORMATION, YOU COULD EVEN WRITE NEW WORKS! THE POSSIBILITIES WERE **ENDLESS!**

NEXT UP, A MULTI-TALENTED GUEST WHOSE PROLIFIC LIST OF PARTICULAR PROFESSIONS WOULD BE ENOUGH TO IMPRESS EVEN THE MOST PERNICKETY OF PEOPLE...

IT'S EXPLORER, GEOGRAPHER, ARTIST, CARTOGRAPHER, GEOLOGIST, BOTANIST, SOCIOLOGIST AND VULCANOLOGIST...

ALEXANDER VON HUMBOLDT!

ALEXANDER VON HUMBOLDT

EXPLORER, NATURALIST, GEOGRAPHER, ETC...

1769–1859

ALEXANDER, YOU'RE BEST KNOWN FOR YOUR SCIENTIFIC EXPLORATIONS IN SOUTH AMERICA AND THE INCREDIBLE NUMBER OF DISCOVERIES THAT YOU MADE...

IN YOUR FIVE-YEAR EXPEDITION, YOU DISCOVERED **3,500** NEW SPECIES, THE MOST EVER ON A SINGLE TRIP!

YES, IT WAS **GLORIOUS**! I COLLECTED **60,000** SAMPLES, AND MADE OVER **400** DRAWINGS.

I WANTED TO UNDERSTAND WHAT I CALLED "HARMONY IN NATURE" – THE INVISIBLE FORCES THAT CONNECT PLANTS, ANIMALS AND THEIR ENVIRONMENT.

FOR EXAMPLE, I WAS THE FIRST TO REALISE THAT SIMILAR HABITATS EXIST ALL AROUND THE WORLD BASED ON HOW WARM OR COOL IT IS...

YOU RETURNED TO EUROPE A **CELEBRITY**! IT'S SAID THAT, AFTER NAPOLEON, YOU WERE THE MOST FAMOUS MAN IN THE WORLD!

I MET HIM ONCE. I THINK HE WAS JEALOUS...

YOU COLLECT **PLANTS**?

PFF...

SO DOES MY **WIFE**!

BUT NO ONE, NOT EVEN **NAPOLEON**, CAN CLAIM TO HAVE AS MANY THINGS NAMED AFTER HIM!

A PENGUIN A SQUID AN OCEAN CURRENT A BAY A DRY LAKE BED FOUR COUNTIES

TWO MOUNTAIN RANGES

A SKUNK A GLACIER

A RIVER DOLPHIN

FOUR TREES

THREE HUNDRED PLANTS

TWO MOUNTAINS THREE PARKS

THIRTEEN TOWNS

A RIVER

A SINKHOLE

A HOTEL

A LUNAR SEA FOUR UNIVERSITIES, TWO COLLEGES AND NINE SCHOOLS

AN ASTEROID

THREE STREETS

IT'S VERY FLATTERING, BUT I REALLY NEVER WANTED ALL THAT ATTENTION...

NICE TO SEE THAT YOU STAYED VON **HUMBLE(DT)**...!

FORTUNATELY, I HAD SOME GREAT FAMILY FRIENDS WHO SAW MY POTENTIAL.

LOOK AT HOW **SMART** THIS GIRL IS!

IT'S A CRIMINAL SHAME.

TOGETHER WE FORMED AN OUTLANDISH PLAN...

I'LL WRITE YOU A RECOMMENDATION. THEY'LL LISTEN TO AN **EARL**!

WHEN VENEZUELA IS FREE, WE'D BE **PROUD** TO HAVE A FEMALE DOCTOR!

I'LL DISGUISE YOU AS MY NEPHEW.

MARY-ANNE BULKLEY, MUM.

DAVID STUART ERSKINE, EARL OF BUCHAN.

GENERAL MIRANDA, VENEZUELEN FREEDOM FIGHTER.

AND SO THAT IS HOW I LEFT LONDON MARGARET ANNE BULKLEY.

AND ARRIVED IN EDINBURGH AS JAMES MIRANDA STUART BARRY.

YOU WERE SOMETHING OF A CHILD PRODIGY, **ACING** YOUR EXAMS AGED JUST **17**, THE YOUNGEST STUDENT EVER TO DO SO!

BUT THEN GENERAL MIRANDA (THE ONLY GUY PREPARED TO EMPLOY WOMEN DOCTORS) GOT **KILLED** WHILE FIGHTING FOR VENEZUELAN FREEDOM. WHICH MADE IT RATHER TRICKY TO GO WORK FOR HIM...

WELL, I WASN'T GOING TO GIVE UP BEING A DOCTOR! SO I FIGURED: I'D JUST HAVE TO CARRY ON BEING A MAN.

I LOOKED AROUND FOR A JOB. TURNS OUT, THE **BRITISH ARMY** NEEDED DOCTORS, AND THEY WEREN'T TOO PICKY WHERE THEY GOT 'EM...

SO NOW YOU HAD TO MAKE A MULTITUDE OF MACHO MILITARY MEN THINK YOU WERE ONE OF THEM. WEREN'T YOU WORRIED SOMEONE WOULD FIND OUT?

PFF! NO PROBLEM!

SEE, I QUICKLY REALISED THAT IN THE ARMY THE KEY THING WASN'T SO MUCH **LOOKING** LIKE A MAN (I JUST HAD TO WEAR THE RIGHT CLOTHES) AS IT WAS **ACTING** LIKE A MAN...

MOST IMPORTANTLY, I HAD TO GET USED TO PICKING FIGHTS, TALKING OVER PEOPLE AND GENERALLY BEING INSUFFERABLY OPINIONATED!

WELL, I THINK...

NONSENSE, MY DEAR FELLOW! TRUST ME. I'M A DOCTOR.

HEE HEE! IT'S REALLY QUITE LIBERATING. YOU SHOULD TRY IT.

WELL, I...

OH WAIT — YOU'RE A MAN. YOU PROBABLY ALREADY DO...

UM... YOU WERE POSTED TO BRITISH SOUTH AFRICA, AND QUICKLY FOUND ALL SORTS OF OPPORTUNITIES TO MAKE USE OF YOUR MAGNIFICENT MEDICAL SKILLS.

YOU WERE ESPECIALLY POPULAR WITH WOMEN, THE POOR AND BLACK PEOPLE — ALL OF WHOM THE OTHER DOCTORS USUALLY IGNORED.

RIGHT. BUT IT WASN'T TILL I SAVED THE LIFE OF THE COLONIAL GOVERNOR THAT I MANAGED TO GET SOME **REAL** CLOUT...

HOW CAN I EVER REPAY YOU?

WELL...

Coff!

Coff!

WITH HIS BACKING, I BECAME THE COLONY'S CHIEF MEDICAL INSPECTOR. AT LAST, EVERYONE WOULD HAVE TO DO WHAT I SAID!

HEH HEH!

AND YOU USED YOUR NEW POSITION OF AUTHORITY TO PUSH THROUGH SOME OF THE MOST IMPORTANT HEALTHCARE REFORMS OF **ALL TIME!**

I'D BEEN STUDYING THE HOSPITAL RECORDS AND I NOTICED THAT MOST PEOPLE WEREN'T DYING FROM **WAR WOUNDS**, BUT FROM DISEASES, LIKE **CHOLERA** OR **TYPHUS**.

AND I'D TRACED THE CAUSE OF THOSE DISEASES TO **POOR HYGIENE**.

THIS HOSPITAL IS A **PIGSTY!**

LITERALLY.

SO I ENFORCED A STRICT CODE OF CLEANLINESS IN EVERY HOSPITAL, PRISON AND ARMY CAMP UNDER MY CONTROL.

AW, WHAT?

AND I DIDN'T STOP THERE, PROMOTING FRESH, HEALTHY FOOD, BANNING POISONOUS FAKE MEDICINES AND FIRING DOCTORS WHO DIDN'T CARE ABOUT THEIR PATIENTS.

BUT NOT EVERYONE WAS HAPPY WITH YOUR REFORMS...

WHAT'S WRONG WITH THE OLD WAYS!?

PFF! MAKING ME LOOK BAD...

MAYBE I **LIKE** BEING DIRTY!

PLUS YOU CONTINUED PICKING FIGHTS AND DISOBEYING ORDERS.

STOP CALLING YOUR BROTHER OFFICERS IDIOTS!

BUT THEY **ARE** IDIOTS!

A ROLLING CAVALCADE OF PROMOTIONS, DEMOTIONS, ACCOLADES AND SCANDALS SAW YOU PING-PONGING AROUND THE BRITISH EMPIRE, SPREADING YOUR RADICAL REFORMS WHEREVER YOU WENT.

WHICH IS HOW YOU RAN ACROSS PIONEERING NURSE **FLORENCE NIGHTINGALE.**

BAH! THAT WOMAN!

HER "HOSPITAL" WAS ONE OF THE WORST I EVER SAW — **UTTERLY FILTHY!** I GAVE HER A RIGHT GOOD PIECE OF MY MIND, I'LL TELL YOU THAT!

WELL, AFTER YOUR RANT, SHE **CLEANED UP** HER ACT AND WENT ON TO FOUND THE MODERN SCIENCE OF NURSING.

MODERN SCIENCE OF **STEALING MY THUNDER,** MORE LIKE IT...

YOU'RE **BOTH** GREAT, FOR DIFFERENT REASONS. SHE WORKED **WITHIN** THE RULES, **PUSHING THE ENVELOPE** OF WHAT WOMEN WERE ALLOWED TO DO...

WHEREAS YOU **TORE UP** THE ENVELOPE AND THREW IT IN THE BIN, AND IN SO DOING, **PROVED** HOW STUPID IT IS TO DIVIDE THE WORLD INTO BOYS' THINGS AND GIRLS' THINGS!

EXACTLY! WHY NOT JUST LET PEOPLE DO WHAT THEY LOVE!?

ESPECIALLY IF WHAT THEY LOVE IS SAVING LIVES, PICKING FIGHTS AND LOOKING **FREAKING AWESOME** IN AN OFFICER'S JACKET...

A HISTORY OF INFECTION

YEAH, SO, I MANAGED TO SAVE A LOT OF LIVES BY ENFORCING **BASIC HYGIENE**. BUT EVEN **I** HAD NO **REAL** IDEA ABOUT WHAT ACTUALLY **CAUSED** THE DISEASES I WAS FIGHTING...

I'D NEVER EVEN **HEARD** OF BACTERIA! LIKE ALL THE DOCTORS IN MY DAY, I FOLLOWED THE **MIASMA** THEORY.

MAKES SENSE, RIGHT!? AND PEOPLE **DID** GET SICK IF THEY WENT NEAR STINKY SEWAGE, RUBBISH OR ROTTING CORPSES, SO IT LOOKED PRETTY CONVINCING.

CONVINCING, BUT **WRONG!** SOMETIMES INFECTIONS SEEMED TO PASS FROM **PERSON TO PERSON**, AT OTHER TIMES THEY COULD **TRAVEL** LONG DISTANCES. ANOTHER THEORY WAS NEEDED!

NOW, WAY BACK IN **1676**, A DUTCH SCIENTIST WITH THE IMPRESSIVE NAME OF **ANTONIE VAN LEEUWENHOEK** HAD SEEN BACTERIA IN HIS OWN **SPIT** USING A HOME-MADE MICROSCOPE.

OH MAN! THAT'S TOTALLY GROSS!

BUT NO ONE REALISED THESE MICROSCOPIC ORGANISMS WERE CONNECTED TO **DISEASE**.

-SIGH- I MET A LOT OF GUYS LIKE THAT...

THE **REAL** ANSWER WASN'T DISCOVERED UNTIL FRENCH SCIENTIST **LOUIS PASTEUR** DID HIS FAMOUS BACTERIA-KILLING EXPERIMENTS.

IF MILK WAS **SEALED** AND **HEATED**, NO **BACTERIA** WOULD BE LEFT TO TURN IT BAD.

IT WAS PROPOSED BY **GALEN**, A FAMOUS DOCTOR DURING THE **ROMAN EMPIRE**, AND IT BASICALLY HADN'T BEEN UPDATED SINCE!

THE IDEA WAS THAT MIASMAS WERE **BAD SMELLS** FLOATING IN THE AIR AND THAT WAS WHAT GOT PEOPLE SICK.

THAT'S WHY THE MEDIEVAL PLAGUE DOCTORS WORE THOSE LONG-BEAKED MASKS FULL OF **FLOWERS**, SO THEY COULDN'T **SMELL** THE MIASMAS.

HEH HEH. **TOTALLY** SAFE...

THEN, IN **1847**, A HUNGARIAN DOCTOR WITH THE EQUALLY IMPRESSIVE NAME OF **IGNAZ SEMMELWEIS** NOTICED THAT WOMEN GIVING BIRTH IN HOSPITAL WERE **WAY** MORE LIKELY TO DIE THAN WOMEN GIVING BIRTH AT HOME.

HE THOUGHT IT MIGHT BE TO DO WITH THE FACT THAT SURGEONS **DIDN'T WASH THEIR HANDS** IN BETWEEN CUTTING UP DEAD BODIES AND ASSISTING IN BIRTHS.

WHICH **SCANDALISED** THE MEDICAL PROFESSION, WHO ROUNDLY CONDEMNED HIM FOR SUGGESTING SOMETHING SO **INSULTING**.

"A DOCTOR IS A GENTLEMAN. AND A GENTLEMAN'S HANDS ARE **ALWAYS** CLEAN..."

AMERICAN DOCTOR **CHARLES MEIGS**.

HIS DISCOVERY CONVINCED THE WORLD THESE BACTERIA THINGIES MIGHT BE IMPORTANT AFTER ALL.

ALL THE MILK WE DRINK TODAY IS **PASTEURISED** TO KILL GERMS THIS WAY.

BEFORE LONG THE BACTERIA BEHIND **ALL SORTS** OF HORRIBLE DISEASES HAD BEEN FOUND. THE MODERN **GERM THEORY** OF DISEASE WAS HERE TO STAY!

I CAN'T HELP BUT NOTICE ALL OF THESE GUYS ARE... WELL... GUYS.

YEAH, I NOTICED THAT TOO. MAYBE IF THEY HADN'T **BANNED WOMEN FROM SCIENCE**, THEY'D HAVE FIGURED IT OUT SOONER...

DARWIN, YOUR THEORY OF EVOLUTION TOTALLY CHANGED HOW WE SEE THE WORLD, AND ALL THE CREATURES IN IT, INCLUDING OURSELVES.

DID YOU ALWAYS PLAN TO BECOME A SCIENTIST?

GOOD **GRIEF** NO! I DIDN'T EVEN KNOW IT WAS SOMETHING YOU COULD **DO**! I JUST LIKED NATURE.

AS A BOY, I WAS ALWAYS INTO EXPLORING NATURE AND COLLECTING STUFF...

BUT, AS I GREW UP, I BECAME MORE INTERESTED IN **HUNTING** ANIMALS THAN IN STUDYING THEM...

MY **DAD** WASN'T TOO PLEASED ABOUT THAT...

GET OUT THERE AND FIND A **PROPER** JOB!

SO HE SENT YOU TO STUDY TO BECOME A **CHURCH MINISTER**...

AH, YES — FUN TIMES...

IT WAS AT COLLEGE THAT I GOT INTO THE WILD, NO-HOLDS-BARRED WORLD OF EXTREME **BEETLE COLLECTING**!

I WAS CONSTANTLY VYING WITH MY FRIENDS TO SEE WHO COULD FIND THE **RAREST** SPECIES!

ONCE, I WAS SUPPOSED TO GO VISIT MY GIRLFRIEND AT THE TIME FOR CHRISTMAS, BUT I WENT OFF TO HUNT BEETLES INSTEAD.

YEAH, SHE DUMPED ME...

...BUT I GOT SOME **SWEET FINDS** FOR MY COLLECTION!

SO, UH, MERRY CHRISTMAS TO ME!

BUT YOU BEGAN TO HUNGER FOR **MORE** THAN JUST THE BIGGEST COLLECTION...

RIGHT. (ALTHOUGH, CAN I JUST SAY, MINE WAS PRETTY FREAKIN' AWESOME...)

I'D BEEN READING STUFF BY GUYS LIKE **ALEXANDER VON HUMBOLDT***, WHO DESCRIBED ALL THE AWESOME STUFF HE'D SEEN IN SOUTH AMERICA.

*SEE PAGE **68**.

AND I STARTED TO WONDER **WHY** ALL THESE PLANTS AND ANIMALS HAD THE DIFFERENT SHAPES, COLOURS AND BEHAVIOURS THAT THEY DID.

THE MAIN THEORY AT THE TIME WAS THAT **GOD** HAD MADE THEM ALL TO PERFECTLY MATCH THE ENVIRONMENT THEY LIVED IN.

AND FOR A WHILE I THOUGHT THAT SOUNDED PRETTY SENSIBLE.

BUT THEN CAME THE EVENT THAT CHANGED YOUR THINKING, AND YOUR LIFE, **FOREVER**.

THE **HMS BEAGLE** WAS GOING ON A ROUND-THE-WORLD MISSION TO MAKE MAPS FOR THE NAVY, AND THEY WANTED A SCIENTIST TO GO ALONG!

HELLO!

NEEEooow!

I GUESS THEY FIGURED, SINCE THEY WERE SAILING TO ALL THOSE FARAWAY PLACES **ANYWAY**, THEY MIGHT AS WELL DO SOME SCIENCE WHILE THEY WERE AT IT...

FOR THE NEXT **5 YEARS** THIS TINY CABIN IN THE BACK OF THE SHIP WAS MY HOME. THERE WAS A PLACE FOR EVERYTHING I NEEDED HERE...

SLEEPING

STUDYING

SPECIMEN STORAGE

BEING SICK

HEEUURGH!

EW! THAT SOUNDS PRETTY NASTY...

IT WAS HORRIBLE! I WAS SEA-SICK FOR PRETTY MUCH THE **WHOLE TIME**!

BUT I DIDN'T LET THAT STOP ME HAVING AN AMAZING **EDUCATIONAL EXPERIENCE**! WHEREVER WE STOPPED, I STUDIED THE WILDLIFE, AND COLLECTED SPECIMENS...

-SIGH- SO MAJESTIC...

80

SQUAWK!

WHAT?! THAT'S HOW WE COLLECTED SPECIMENS BACK THEN!

BUT IT WAS MY TIME IN THE **GALAPAGOS ISLANDS**, OFF THE PACIFIC COAST OF SOUTH AMERICA, THAT **REALLY** GOT ME THINKING...

THE GALAPAGOS ISLANDS HAVE ALL THESE WEIRD ANIMALS THAT ARE FOUND **NOWHERE ELSE**: GIANT TORTOISES, FLIGHTLESS CORMORANTS, MARINE IGUANAS...

WOO! YEAH!

SCIENCE!

ALL THESE CREATURES WERE SIMILAR TO, BUT NOT THE SAME AS, ONES I FOUND ON THE SOUTH AMERICAN MAINLAND.

THE LOCAL INHABITANTS COULD EVEN TELL **WHICH** ISLAND A TORTOISE CAME FROM.

MM... DEFINITELY A **JAMES** ISLAND...

I STARTED TO WONDER IF THEY MIGHT HAVE COME FROM THE MAINLAND A LONG TIME AGO, GOT **ISOLATED** ON THE ISLANDS AND THEN SLOWLY CHANGED INTO THE NEW SPECIES WE SEE TODAY.

THAT'S THE FIRST PART OF YOUR **THEORY OF EVOLUTION!**

RIGHT — SPECIES CHANGE OVER TIME. BUT HOW? AND **WHY?**

HUMANS HAVE BEEN DOING BASICALLY THE SAME THING FOR THOUSANDS OF YEARS TO OUR **DOMESTICATED** ANIMALS! SO WHEN I GOT HOME, I STARTED ASKING **ANIMAL BREEDERS** ABOUT THEIR WORK.

LOOK AT SOMETHING LIKE THE **PIGEON!** WILD PIGEONS ALL LOOK MUCH THE SAME...

81

BUT SOME INDIVIDUALS HAVE SLIGHTLY POOFIER FEATHERS, OR REDDER EYES, OR WHATEVER...

BY **SELECTING** WHICH BIRDS TO BREED, PIGEON BREEDERS CAN, OVER MANY GENERATIONS, CREATE **TOTALLY** DIFFERENT-LOOKING CREATURES.

I MEAN, SERIOUSLY, LOOK AT SOME OF THESE FREAKY THINGS!

SO YOU FIGURED **NATURE** MIGHT BE DOING THE SAME THING, JUST OVER A **REALLY** LONG TIME.

I WAS READING A BOOK BY A GUY CALLED **THOMAS MALTHUS** ABOUT HOW, IF THERE ARE TOO MANY PEOPLE, AND NOT ENOUGH FOOD, SOME OF THOSE PEOPLE ARE GONNA STARVE.

WOW. SOUNDS LIKE SOME CHEERY BEDTIME READING...

YEAH, BUT HE'S RIGHT, THOUGH.

THERE'S ALWAYS GOING TO BE MORE ANIMALS BORN THAN CAN GROW UP AND HAVE CHILDREN OF THEIR OWN...

LOTS OF THEM WILL STARVE, OR GET EATEN, OR DIE OF ILLNESS OR WHATEVER...

THIS IS GETTING MORE AND MORE MORBID. SO WHO LIVES AND WHO DIES, THEN?

WELL, JUST LIKE WITH THE PIGEONS, EACH INDIVIDUAL ANIMAL WILL BE SLIGHTLY DIFFERENT FROM THE NEXT...

OK, THINK ABOUT PEOPLE. SOME PEOPLE ARE NATURALLY TALLER THAN OTHERS, RIGHT?

AND TALL PEOPLE ARE GENERALLY BETTER AT BASKETBALL, RIGHT?

UH SURE, I GUESS...

SOME ALIENS ARRIVE AND MAKE EVERYONE PLAY BASKETBALL. AND IF YOU LOSE A GAME, THEY KILL YOU...

GOOD GRIEF! WHAT?!

IT'S AN EXAMPLE. JUST ROLL WITH IT.

THE TALL PEOPLE ARE MORE LIKELY TO SURVIVE AND HAVE TALL KIDS, RIGHT?

EXCEPT, IF **EVERYONE** IS TALL, SUDDENLY YOU NEED TO BE **EVEN TALLER** TO WIN AT BASKETBALL.

SO OVER TIME, THE ENTIRE HUMAN POPULATION WILL GET TALLER (AND BETTER AT BASKETBALL).

NEAT, EH?

AND THIS COULD HAPPEN WITH **ANY** USEFUL FEATURE: A BIGGER BEAK, FASTER RUN, STRONGER POISON; WHATEVER!

OK. I GUESS... BUT THAT JUST EXPLAINS HOW ONE TYPE OF ANIMAL CAN CHANGE. WHAT ABOUT COMING UP WITH A TOTALLY **NEW** SPECIES?

WELL, ACTUALLY, I EXPLAINED MY THEORY ABOUT THAT IN MY BOOK "ON THE ORIGIN OF SPECIES" (AVAILABLE FROM ALL GOOD BOOKSHOPS...).

TAKE **BEARS**, FOR EXAMPLE. SOME BEARS SWIM AROUND WITH THEIR MOUTHS OPEN, SCOOPING UP INSECTS ON THE WATER'S SURFACE.

NOW, IT DOESN'T TAKE MUCH TO IMAGINE THAT A BIG MOUTH WOULD HELP WITH THIS. SO, OVER MANY GENERATIONS, THEIR MOUTHS MIGHT GET BIGGER.

PLUS THEY WOULD BE CONSTANTLY GETTING WATER UP THEIR NOSES, SO A BEAR WITH HIS NOSE JUST A LITTLE HIGHER UP WOULD DO BETTER.

SO, JUST LIKE WITH THE BASKETBALL PLAYERS GETTING TALLER, THEIR NOSES MIGHT MOVE UP TO THE TOP OF THEIR HEADS...

AND IF THEY WERE SWIMMING ALL THE TIME, BEARS WITH FLATTER, MORE PADDLE-LIKE FEET WOULD SWIM BETTER.

SO, OVER A LONG, LONG TIME, THEY MIGHT EVOLVE INTO SOMETHING LIKE A **WHALE**!

ACTUALLY, I GOT MADE FUN OF **SO MUCH** FOR THAT PARTICULAR IDEA, I HAD TO TAKE IT OUT OF LATER EDITIONS OF MY BOOK.

HAR HAR!

WHALES INDEED!

HEY DARWIN, GRIN AND **BEAR** IT!

WHICH IS A SHAME, BECAUSE WE'VE ACTUALLY FOUND FOSSILS SHOWING **EXACTLY** THAT EVOLUTIONARY TRANSITION, NOT FROM BEARS, BUT FROM AN ANCIENT RELATIVE OF THE HIPPO.

YESS! I KNEW iT! EAT IT, HATERS!

ACTUALLY, I MEAN -ER- HOW **EDIFYING** TO FIND SUCH EXCELLENT SUPPORTING EVIDENCE.

QUITE.

BUT THERE **WAS** A **REAL BACKLASH** AGAINST YOUR WORK, AND NOT JUST ABOUT THE BEAR THING...

LOTS OF PEOPLE TOOK OFFENCE AT THE IDEA THAT THEY WERE DESCENDED FROM PREHISTORIC APES.

THE VERY THOUGHT!

DASHED RUDE, I CALL IT!

ALTHOUGH WE **HAVE** FOUND FOSSILS THAT SHOW EXACTLY THAT TRANSITION AS WELL...

I WONDER, WITH SOME OF THESE PEOPLE, IF THEY REALISE WHAT AN **INSANELY** LONG PERIOD OF TIME WE'RE TALKING ABOUT HERE...

I MEAN, IT'S BEEN **1,500** YEARS SINCE THE FALL OF THE ROMAN EMPIRE — THAT'S A LONG TIME! IT'S MAYBE **75** GENERATIONS OF PEOPLE.

SINCE THE FIRST MODERN HUMANS, THERE'S BEEN SOMETHING LIKE **10,000** GENERATIONS. THAT'S **130** TIMES LONGER!

BUT THAT'S **NOTHING!** IT'S LITERALLY **NOT LONG ENOUGH** FOR ANY EVOLUTION TO HAPPEN, SINCE WE'RE PRETTY MUCH THE SAME, BIOLOGICALLY, AS THOSE FIRST PEOPLE...

THE SPLIT BETWEEN THE ANCESTORS OF HUMANS AND CHIMPS, WAS **50** TIMES LONGER THAN **THAT!**

SEE YA.

AND EVEN **THAT'S** NOT MUCH, SINCE WE SHARE **99%** OF OUR DNA WITH CHIMPS! SINCE THE FIRST PRIMATES IT'S BEEN...

STOP STOP! YOU'RE MAKING ME DIZZY.

I GUESS THE POINT IS: THE WORLD WASN'T MADE SPECIALLY FOR US. WE JUST **HAPPEN** TO BE HERE...

JUST LIKE EVERYTHING ELSE.

85

WHO'S THE MAN WHO UNCOVERED THE **FUNDAMENTAL LAWS OF CHEMISTRY** AND USED THEM TO ARRANGE THE **PERIODIC TABLE?**

ELEMENTARY! IT'S THE MOST FAMOUS SCIENTIST YOU'VE **NEVER** HEARD OF...

DMITRI MENDELEEV!

DMITRI MENDELEEV
CHEMIST
1834–1907

PROFESSOR MENDELEEV, YOUR STORY BEGINS IN THE WILD ARCTIC WASTES OF **SIBERIA**, WHERE YOU WERE THE YOUNGEST OF **17 CHILDREN!**

HEH HEH. MEALTIMES WERE PRETTY CRAZY AT OUR HOUSE...

MOST OF THE OTHERS HAD GROWN UP AND LEFT HOME WHEN THE TRAGEDIES STARTED...

TRAGEDIES!?

TRAGEDIES.

FIRST, PAPPA WENT BLIND. TO SUPPORT US, MAMMA TOOK OVER THE RUNNING OF THE FAMILY **GLASS FACTORY**.

IT WAS THERE THAT I BECAME FASCINATED WITH ALL THE WEIRD AND WONDERFUL BOTTLES AND BEAKERS WE MADE FOR CHEMISTRY EXPERIMENTS.

BUT THEN PAPPA DIED AND THE FACTORY BURNED DOWN.

OH, GEEZ. AT THE SAME TIME?

PRETTY CLOSE.

THEN, WHILE I WAS AT UNIVERSITY, MAMMA AND MY SISTERS DIED OF **TUBERCULOSIS**.

IT ALMOST KILLED ME, TOO. THE DOCTORS GAVE ME A YEAR TO LIVE.

BUT I SURVIVED AND SWORE FROM THEN ON TO DEDICATE MY LIFE TO **SCIENCE**.

I RESEARCHED ALL SORTS OF THINGS, FROM ALCOHOL TO FERTILISERS TO OIL. BUT IT WASN'T ENOUGH JUST TO STUDY. I ALSO WANTED TO **TEACH**, TO SHARE MY KNOWLEDGE AND MY LOVE OF SCIENCE!

WHENEVER I TRAVELLED BY TRAIN, I ALWAYS WENT THIRD CLASS WITH THE POOR FARMERS, SO I COULD TELL THEM ABOUT THE LATEST AGRICULTURE RESEARCH.

I WAS TEACHING UNIVERSITY STUDENTS, TOO. BUT THERE WASN'T A CHEMISTRY TEXTBOOK IN **RUSSIAN**. SO I DECIDED TO WRITE MY OWN.

I WAS WRITING ABOUT THE ELEMENTS, WHEN I STARTED NOTICING SOME CURIOUS PATTERNS...

WAIT A MINUTE, WAIT A MINUTE. **ELEMENTS**. WHAT **ARE** ELEMENTS?

ELEMENTS ARE LIKE THE LETTERS OF THE ALPHABET, SIMPLE CHEMICALS THAT CAN COMBINE TO MAKE MORE COMPLICATED 'WORDS'.

H (HYDROGEN)
H (HYDROGEN)
O (OXYGEN)
H_2O (WATER)

SOME ELEMENTS, LIKE SODIUM OR POTASSIUM, **EXPLODE** ON CONTACT WITH AIR OR WATER!

LOTS ARE HARD, SHINY AND GOOD CONDUCTORS OF **ELECTRICITY** – THE METALS.

SOME, LIKE OXYGEN OR CARBON, **DON'T** CONDUCT ELECTRICITY, BUT THEY ARE GREAT AT COMBINING WITH OTHER ELEMENTS TO MAKE NEW THINGS.

YOUR BODY IS MOSTLY CARBON AND OXYGEN.

I KNEW THERE MUST BE SOME PATTERN, SOME REASON WHY THEY SHARED SIMILAR PROPERTIES LIKE THAT, BUT **WHAT?**

I HAD THEM ALL WRITTEN OUT ON CARDS, AND I'D SPENT **YEARS** MOVING THEM AROUND, ARRANGING AND REARRANGING...

BORON HERE...

NO, WAIT, **ANTIMONY** HERE, BORON THERE...

BUT THEN, ONE DAY, I GOT **SO SLEEPY**, I HAD TO TAKE A NAP.

CALCIUM...

NICKEL...

MOLYBDENUM...

Z

AND THERE, IN MY DREAM, I SAW IT ALL LAID OUT!

AS YOU GO ALONG THE ROWS, THE SIZE OF THE ATOMS GOES UP.

THIS GROUPS THE SIMILAR ELEMENTS IN COLUMNS.

WHY DO THE ROWS GET LONGER? **I DON'T KNOW!** MAYBE YOUR MODERN SCIENCE HAS THE ANSWER...

I HAD TO LEAVE SOME **GAPS.** WERE THERE **NEW ELEMENTS** WE HADN'T FOUND YET?

EXPLOSIVE CHEMICALS   METALS   NON-METALS

HUH!? WUZZAT!

NOT EVERYONE LIKED MY NEW SYSTEM...

WHAT'S WITH ALL THE **GAPS**, HUH? **MENDELEEEV?**

BUT WHEN THE MISSING ELEMENTS WERE FOUND, THEY HAD TO ACCEPT MY SYSTEM WAS RIGHT!

GALLIUM

Ga

FOUND 1875

GERMANIUM

Ge

FOUND 1886

SCANDIUM

Sn

FOUND 1879

Ga Ge

BUT, EVEN AS YOUR DISCOVERY ROCKED THE SCIENTIFIC COMMUNITY, YOUR PRIVATE LIFE WAS ROCKED BY **SCANDAL**!

AND I DON'T MEAN YOUR SCANDALOUS **HAIR**, WHICH YOU ONLY CUT ONCE A YEAR!

HEY!

BUT THE SCANDAL OF YOU DIVORCING YOUR WIFE TO MARRY A YOUNG ART STUDENT **HALF YOUR AGE**!

BOT!

YEAH... DIVORCE PRETTY MUCH WASN'T ALLOWED BACK THEN, BUT I GOT SPECIAL PERMISSION FROM THE **TSAR**.

WHICH LED TO LOTS OF OTHER PEOPLE WHO HATED THEIR WIVES TRYING IT, TOO...

GET OUT OF HERE! I HAVE PLENTY OF YOU FOOLS, BUT ONLY ONE MENDELEEV!

SERIOUSLY, THOUGH, HOW'D AN OLD MARRIED GUY WITH **THAT BEARD** MANAGE TO CONVINCE SUCH A BEAUTY TO MARRY HIM ANYWAY?

HEY! I **LIKE** THIS BEARD!

AND I WAS **VERY** PERSUASIVE...

IF YOU DON'T MARRY ME, I'LL **KILL MYSELF**!

ALL RIGHT! I'LL DO IT... FOR **SCIENCE**.

INCREDIBLY, AFTER SUCH A DRAMATIC START, YOU HAD A VERY HAPPY MARRIAGE.

WHAT CAN I SAY? WE HAD CHEMISTRY.

GEDDIT!? **CHEMISTRY**!?

PERIODIC TABLE

AND NOW, PLEASE WELCOME TO THE GRAVEYARD A GUEST WHO COMES WITH **GLOWING RECOMMENDATIONS**...

IT'S THE **MOTHER OF INVENTION**; TWO-TIME NOBEL PRIZE WINNER...

MARIE CURIE!

MARIE CURIE

CHEMIST & PHYSICIST

1867-1934

NOW, YOU MIGHT SPOT SOMETHING **DIFFERENT** ABOUT ME IN THIS INTERVIEW...

AND NO, IT'S NOT MY NEW HAIRCUT.

(THANKS FOR NOTICING THOUGH.)

MARIE, WITH HER HUSBAND PIERRE, DISCOVERED **RADIATION**. TURNS OUT, IT'S DEADLY!

HENCE THE SUIT.

WE DIDN'T KNOW...

MARIE, TIMES WERE TOUGH IN **POLAND** WHEN YOU WERE A GIRL...

THAT'S FOR SURE! BACK THEN, THE **RUSSIANS** RULED POLAND...

AND ONE OF THEIR RULES WAS THAT **NO POLES** WERE ALLOWED TO GET AN **EDUCATION**.

I WASN'T GOING TO LET **THAT** STOP ME! I STUDIED SCIENCE AT A **TOP SECRET UNDERGROUND UNIVERSITY!**

PASSWORD?

I ♥ SCIENCE.

BUT TO LEARN THE REALLY **CUTTING-EDGE** SCIENCE, I HAD TO GO TO THE **NUMBER ONE** UNIVERSITY, AND THAT WAS IN **PARIS!**

I WAS SO **POOR**, I COULD ONLY AFFORD A TINY ATTIC. IT GOT **SO COLD**, I USED TO SLEEP WITH **ALL** MY CLOTHES ON!

BUT HOW **WONDERFUL**, POOR AND ALONE AS I WAS, TO STUDY IN THE **CAPITAL** OF **SCIENCE!**

BUT YOU WEREN'T ALONE FOR LONG...

YES, WELL, THAT'S WHERE I MET **PIERRE**...

WINK WINK

HE WAS AN EXTRAORDINARY MAN, AS TOTALLY DEDICATED TO SCIENCE AS I WAS.

AW! SO ROMANTIC!

WE GOT MARRIED AND STARTED ON OUR RESEARCH.

AT THE TIME, **X-RAYS** WERE THE NEW **HOT SCIENCE.**

I SAY!

SPLENDID!

A FRENCH SCIENTIST NAMED LOUIS BECQUEREL HAD DISCOVERED ANOTHER TYPE OF RAY GIVEN OFF BY **URANIUM**...

SACRE BLEU!

EVEN THOUGH THE WORLD IGNORED HIS DISCOVERY, I WAS **FASCINATED** BY BECQUEREL'S RAYS, AND I MADE AN **AMAZING** DISCOVERY...

SCIENTISTS HAD ALWAYS THOUGHT THAT **ATOMS** WERE THE SMALLEST THINGS THAT EXISTED...

BUT I DISCOVERED THAT THE RAYS WERE COMING FROM **INSIDE** THE ATOM!

WE CALLED THE RAYS **"RADIATION"**.

AND THEIR DISCOVERY **REVOLUTIONISED** THE WORLD!

THIS WAS THE BIRTH OF **NUCLEAR SCIENCE!**

$E=MC^2$

PIERRE AND I WERE AWARDED OUR FIRST NOBEL PRIZE IN **1903**. LIFE WAS GOOD, BUT THEN...

TRAGEDY STRUCK! PIERRE WAS **KILLED** WHEN HE SLIPPED AND FELL UNDER A SPEEDING CART.

MY DEAR PIERRE! HE WAS PROBABLY THINKING ABOUT SCIENCE AND NOT PAYING ATTENTION. MY FRIEND, LOVER, COMPANION, GONE FOREVER!

BUT LIFE DIDN'T END THERE. I KEPT WORKING ON OUR RESEARCH, AND EVENTUALLY, WAS ABLE TO FOUND A **RESEARCH INSTITUTE** WORTHY OF HIS MEMORY.

AND IT WAS MANY YEARS BEFORE **YOU** DIED, FINALLY SUCCUMBING TO THE EFFECTS OF ALL THAT **RADIATION**...

ALL RIGHT! WE DIDN'T KNOW!

HANG ON, IF YOU'RE **RADIOACTIVE**, DOES THAT MEAN YOU HAVE **AWESOME SUPERPOWERS**!?

WHAT!? NO! THAT ONLY HAPPENS IN COMIC BOOKS!

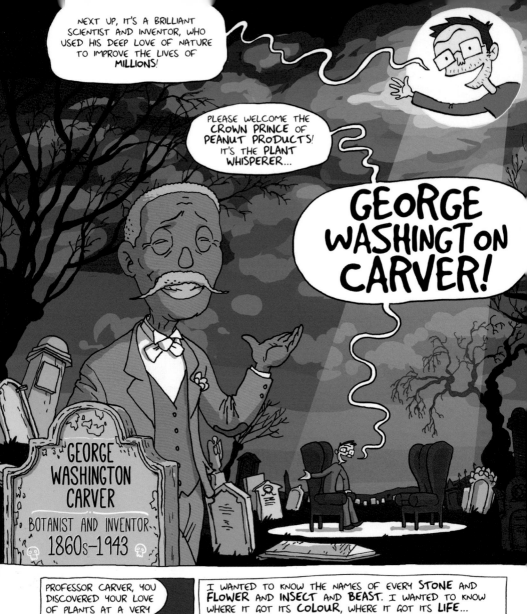

NEXT UP, IT'S A BRILLIANT SCIENTIST AND INVENTOR, WHO USED HIS DEEP LOVE OF NATURE TO IMPROVE THE LIVES OF MILLIONS!

PLEASE WELCOME THE CROWN PRINCE OF PEANUT PRODUCTS! IT'S THE PLANT WHISPERER...

GEORGE WASHINGTON CARVER!

GEORGE WASHINGTON CARVER
BOTANIST AND INVENTOR
1860s–1943

PROFESSOR CARVER, YOU DISCOVERED YOUR LOVE OF PLANTS AT A VERY EARLY AGE.

YES, I USED TO GO WALKING IN THE WOODS NEAR THE FARM WHERE I LIVED...

I WANTED TO KNOW THE NAMES OF EVERY STONE AND FLOWER AND INSECT AND BEAST. I WANTED TO KNOW WHERE IT GOT ITS COLOUR, WHERE IT GOT ITS LIFE...

BUT THERE WAS NO ONE TO TELL ME.

COULDN'T YOU ASK YOUR PARENTS?

I NEVER KNEW THEM.

MY PARENTS WERE **SLAVES** IN AMERICA — BELONGING TO A FARMER CALLED MOSES CARVER.

POPPA DIED BEFORE I WAS BORN. MY MOMMA AND I GOT **STOLEN** BY **SLAVE RAIDERS** WHEN I WAS JUST A BABY.

MR CARVER TRADED A **HORSE** TO GET ME BACK, BUT THEY'D ALREADY **SOLD** MY MOMMA. I NEVER SAW HER AGAIN.

I STAYED ON AT CARVER'S FARM, AND IT WAS THERE THAT I DISCOVERED I COULD USE MY **PLANT POWERS** TO HELP PEOPLE OUT!

WITH ALL THE TIME I SPENT TALKING TO THE PLANTS, I KNEW A LOT ABOUT WHAT THEY LIKED AND HOW TO HELP THEM GROW.

SO I ALSO KNEW HOW TO HELP OUT FOLKS IF THEY HAD SICK PLANTS. THEY USED TO CALL ME THE **PLANT DOCTOR.**

I WANTED TO KEEP ON LEARNING, BUT THEY WOULDN'T ALLOW BLACK FOLKS TO STUDY AT THE LOCAL SCHOOL. SO I SET OFF WALKING TO FIND ONE THAT DID!

THAT WAS HOW I MET MISS **MARIAH WATKINS.** SHE WAS A NICE LADY WHO OWNED THE BARN I HAD BEEN SLEEPING IN...

I NEVER FORGOT WHAT SHE SAID.

YOU MUST LEARN ALL YOU CAN, THEN GO BACK OUT INTO THE WORLD AND GIVE YOUR LEARNING BACK TO THE PEOPLE.

WHICH YOU DID, BECOMING A PROFESSOR OF **BOTANY**. AND IT WASN'T LONG BEFORE YOU FOUND SOME MORE **PLANT PROBLEMS** TO HELP WITH...

WELL, AT THAT TIME THERE WAS A BIG PROBLEM IN THE SOUTH. YOU SEE, ALL THE BLACK FOLKS THAT USED TO BE SLAVES WERE NOW FREE FARMERS.

WHICH **SHOULD** HAVE BEEN GREAT, EXCEPT THAT THEY ONLY HAD EXPERIENCE WITH GROWING COTTON.

AND COTTON **DEPLETES** THE SOIL, SO AFTER A FEW YEARS THERE'S NO NUTRIENTS LEFT AND THE CROPS ALL DIE.

I REALISED THEY COULD PLANT **OTHER** CROPS, THINGS THAT GROW NATIVE IN THE SOUTH, THAT WOULD PUT NUTRIENTS **BACK INTO** THE SOIL.

CROPS LIKE **PEANUTS**!

I HAD A LITTLE WAGON THAT I DROVE AROUND, TEACHING FOLKS HOW TO USE THIS **CROP ROTATION SYSTEM**.

SOON PEOPLE ALL OVER THE SOUTH WERE GROWING PEANUTS! ONLY ONE PROBLEM...

NO ONE **WANTS** ALL THESE PEANUTS! WHAT AM I GOING TO **DO** WITH THEM?!

UM... **EAT** THEM?

THAT'S THE THING. BACK THEN, PEOPLE DIDN'T EAT PEANUTS! SO I GOT IN THE LAB AND STARTED **INVENTING**.

I DISCOVERED OVER **300** PEANUT INVENTIONS, INCLUDING: PEANUT INK, PEANUT SOAP, PEANUT MILK, PEANUT CHEESE, PEANUT COFFEE, PEANUT MAYONNAISE AND PEANUT PEPPER.

SIP

OK, SOME OF THEM WERE PRETTY GROSS. BUT THERE WAS **ONE** PEANUT INVENTION THAT WAS **REALLY** POPULAR...

WAA?!

WAIT, YOU MEAN **YOU'RE** THE REASON WE EAT PEANUT BUTTER?

MIND... BLOWN!

WELL, I JUST HAD A HELPING HAND IN THAT ONE, BUT I ALSO DISCOVERED THINGS YOU COULD MAKE FROM **OTHER** PLANTS, LIKE RUBBER FROM SWEET POTATOES, OR HIGHWAY PAVING FROM PECANS...

WOW — ALL THESE INVENTIONS MUST'VE MADE YOU REALLY **RICH**!

HEH HEH. RICH IN **SPIRIT** MAYBE, BUT NOT IN MONEY. I NEVER REALLY CARED ABOUT THAT.

THOMAS EDISON, THE FAMOUS INVENTOR OF THE LIGHT BULB, WANTED TO PAY ME **BIG BUCKS** TO MAKE INVENTIONS FOR HIM...

BUT HE WANTED TO KEEP THEM ALL FOR HIMSELF, AND MAKE PEOPLE **PAY** TO USE THEM.

HEH HEH HEH

I BELIEVED MY DISCOVERIES WERE A **GIFT FROM GOD**, TALKING TO ME THROUGH HIS PLANTS. YOU CAN'T **SELL** SOMETHING LIKE THAT!

WELL, LET'S ALL GIVE THANKS FOR THE WONDERFUL GIFT OF PEANUT BUTTER!

OOH THANK YOU THANK YOU OM NOM NOM NOM!

NUTS ABOUT NUTS!

PEANUTS ARE **DRY ROASTED**. A ROTATING DRUM ENSURES THE PEANUTS ALL COOK EXACTLY THE SAME.

ONCE THEY'RE DONE THEY ARE **SPEED-COOLED** BY SUCKING OUT THE HOT AIR.

THE PEANUTS ARE **BLANCHED** IN SUPER HOT WATER AND THEN ROLLED TO REMOVE THEIR SKINS.

FINALLY THEY ARE **GROUND** INTO BUTTER.

CRUNCHY PEANUT BUTTER IS MADE BY ADDING SMALL PEANUT BITS BACK INTO THE SMOOTH PASTE.

THEN AT LONG, **LONG** LAST THE PEANUT BUTTER IS PIPED INTO **JARS**, READY FOR EATING.

BUT EVEN BEING A **GENIUS** WILL ONLY TAKE YOU SO FAR — SOMETIMES THE **REALLY** GREAT IDEAS JUST SEEM TO COME WHEN THEY WANT TO...

I'D BE PUZZLING OVER SOMETHING FOR MONTHS, EVEN **YEARS**, AND THEN SUDDENLY THE ANSWER WOULD APPEAR, LITERALLY, IN FRONT OF MY EYES!

AH YES! I SEE IT ALL!

UH, COULD YOU HAVE YOUR VISIONARY EXPERIENCE OVER THERE?

TRAM STOP

YOU WENT TO AMERICA TO WORK FOR THE FAMOUS LIGHTBULB INVENTOR **THOMAS EDISON.**

MUST'VE BEEN NICE TO WORK WITH A KINDRED VISIONARY?

THAT MAN!? BAH! HE WAS THE **WORST!**

NEVER USED HIS BRAIN **AT ALL** IF HE COULD AVOID IT. DO YOU KNOW HE TRIED **6,000** DIFFERENT MATERIALS TO FIND THE FILAMENT FOR HIS LIGHTBULBS?

DON'T THINK THIS ONE WILL WORK, BOSS.

JUST TRY IT!

BUT IT WASN'T JUST THE LIGHTBULBS; HIS WHOLE SYSTEM NEEDED SCRAPPING AND STARTING OVER!

SO I QUIT AND STARTED MY OWN COMPANY TO DO JUST THAT.

EDISON USED LOW-VOLTAGE **DIRECT CURRENT** ELECTRICITY, WHICH IS **SO INEFFICIENT,** HE NEEDED TO BUILD A NEW POWER STATION EVERY **2 MILES** TO TOP UP ALL THE POWER IT LOST.

I INVENTED A NEW **ALTERNATING CURRENT** SYSTEM THAT USES **SUPER-HIGH VOLTAGES,** WHICH CAN BE TRANSMITTED FOR THOUSANDS OF MILES WITH MINIMAL WASTAGE.

WAIT, ISN'T HIGH-VOLTAGE ELECTRICITY **DANGEROUS!?**

BAH! THAT'S WHAT EDISON SAID...

HE WAS SO THREATENED BY MY **SUPERIOR** SYSTEM, HE WENT AROUND **ELECTROCUTING ANIMALS** TO SCARE PEOPLE AWAY FROM IT!

NOW, EXPERIENCE THE SHOCKING HORROR OF **TESLA'S TERROR!**

OOH! SO DANGEROUS!

NOT JUST MANIPULATIVE, BUT ALSO **BAD SCIENCE.** ELECTRICITY HAS MANY ASPECTS: NOT JUST VOLTAGE, BUT ALSO CURRENT, POWER, FREQUENCY, AND SO ON.

WITH THE CORRECT CONFIGURATION, EVEN VERY HIGH VOLTAGES **CAN** BE SAFE, AS I EXHIBITED IN MY OWN LITTLE DEMONSTRATIONS...

OOH! SO SAFE!

IN THE END, YOUR **INTELLIGENT ENGINEERING** WON OUT OVER EDISON'S **UNDERHANDED FEARMONGERING** AND BECAME THE STANDARD SYSTEM USED ALL OVER THE WORLD.

IT ALSO MADE YOU **SO RICH,** YOU COULD START YOUR **OWN** LAB AND FINALLY LET YOUR INCREDIBLE INVENTING IMAGINATION RUN WILD!

MANY OF YOUR MOST INFLUENTIAL INNOVATIONS WERE FIRST DEVELOPED DURING THIS PRODUCTIVE PERIOD.

FLUORESCENT LIGHTS

REMOTE CONTROL

X-RAYS

LASERS

EVEN **MICROWAVES,** ALTHOUGH IT WAS DECADES BEFORE ANYONE THOUGHT OF COOKING WITH THEM.

BUT YOUR GREAT PASSION WAS FOR **WIRELESS COMMUNICATIONS.**

ANOTHER AREA WHERE WE HAVE ONLY JUST CAUGHT UP!

ACTUALLY, YOU'VE NOT CAUGHT UP YET. OH SURE, YOU HAVE **WIFI** (SENDING WIRELESS INFORMATION THROUGH THE AIR)...

BUT YOU STILL NEED TO PLUG YOUR PHONE IN TO CHARGE IT...

MY PLAN WAS TO TRANSMIT **WIRELESS POWER,** ELECTRICITY **ANYONE** COULD USE, **ANYWHERE** IN THE WORLD.

YOU CONVINCED BILLIONAIRE **J.P. MORGAN** TO **FUND** THE MASSIVE PROJECT, WHICH INCLUDED A GIANT TRANSMISSION TOWER TO BEAM ENERGY AROUND THE WORLD...

UNTIL HE REALISED YOU WERE PLANNING TO GIVE THE POWER AWAY FOR **FREE.**

IF THERE'S NO **WIRES,** WHERE DO WE PUT THE **METER?**

CLOSED

ALSO IT'S POSSIBLE IT WOULDN'T HAVE WORKED ANYWAY, BUT THAT IS **NOT THE POINT.**

IT WAS A CRUSHING BLOW. MY DREAMS, **YEARS** OF RESEARCH, AND ALL MY **MONEY** (WHICH I'D ALSO INVESTED) WENT UP IN SMOKE!

YOU CONTINUED TO WORK, BUT YOUR NEW "INVENTIONS" (MANY OF WHICH EXISTED ONLY IN YOUR HEAD) WERE INCREASINGLY HARD TO BELIEVE.

WHATEVER DO YOU MEAN?

AND NOW, THE MATHEMATICAL MAGICIAN WHO **MADE MINCEMEAT** OF THE NASTY NAZIS' **CUTTING-EDGE CRYPTOGRAPHY**, WINNING THE WAR AND GIVING BIRTH TO THE MODERN **COMPUTER AGE** IN THE PROCESS...

PLEASE WELCOME THE BRACINGLY BRILLIANT **BRAIN OF BRITAIN**...

ALAN TURING!

ALAN TURING
COMPUTER SCIENTIST
1912–1954

ALAN, YOU WERE A RATHER OBSCURE MATHEMATICIAN AT CAMBRIDGE UNIVERSITY WHEN THE WAR STARED, HARDLY A LIKELY CANDIDATE FOR A NAZI-SMASHING HERO!

WELL, THERE'S MORE THAN ONE WAY TO WIN A WAR! I WAS STATIONED AT **BLETCHLEY PARK**, WITH A TEAM OF BRITAIN'S MOST BRILLIANT MATHEMATICAL MINDS.

IT WAS BRAINS, NOT BRAWN, THAT COUNTED AT BLETCHLEY. WE WERE ON AN ULTRA-TOP-SECRET CODE-BREAKING MISSION TO DEFEAT THE NAZIS' **ULTIMATE WEAPON**...

THE ENIGMA MACHINE!

IT... ER... DOESN'T **LOOK** LIKE MUCH OF A WEAPON. MORE LIKE A GIANT **TYPEWRITER**...

AHA! BUT IT'S AN **INFORMATION** WEAPON. THINK ABOUT THIS...

THE ENTIRE GERMAN ARMY, NAVY AND AIR FORCE WAS CONSTANTLY SENDING RADIO MESSAGES IN **MORSE CODE**...

ATTACK AT DAWN

BUT **WE** COULD HEAR THEIR MESSAGES TOO, SO WE COULD **WARN** OUR GUYS!

ATTACK AT DAWN

GET OUT OF THERE!

THAT'S WHERE **ENIGMA** CAME IN! THE GERMANS WOULD TYPE A MESSAGE INTO ENIGMA FIRST, AND THE MACHINE WOULD CONVERT IT INTO SCRAMBLED NONSENSE.

ATTACK AT DAWN → CJMCOI XI YZUJ

EVEN IF WE MANAGED TO LISTEN IN TO THE GERMANS' RADIO MESSAGE, WE'D HAVE NO IDEA WHAT IT MEANT.

CJMCOI XI YZUJ

BUT THE GERMANS AT THE OTHER END WOULD TYPE THE NONSENSE INTO **ANOTHER** ENIGMA MACHINE, WHICH WOULD **DE-SCRAMBLE** IT.

ATTACK AT DAWN

HA HA!

SO, ALL YOU NEEDED TO DO WAS **CAPTURE** AN ENIGMA MACHINE OF YOUR OWN, AND YOU COULD TRANSLATE THEIR MESSAGES TOO.

AH! NOT SO FAST...

DEPENDING ON HOW YOU SET UP THE COGS AND WIRES IN THE MACHINE, IT WOULD GIVE A **DIFFERENT** SCRAMBLED MESSAGE.

ATTACK AT DAWN → CJMCOI XI YZUJ

→ ERSJQH SA KHOT

AND THERE WERE **150 MILLION, MILLION, MILLION** SETTINGS! IT WOULD TAKE **DECADES** TO CHECK THEM ALL.

BUT THE GERMANS CHANGED THEIR SETTINGS EVERY **DAY**!

EXACTLY!

THE TROUBLE WAS — OUR HUMAN BRAINS JUST AREN'T **FAST** ENOUGH TO CHECK ALL THE POSSIBILITES. BUT I HAD AN IDEA, BASED ON MY WORK BEFORE THE WAR...

TWO OBSCURE VICTORIAN MATHEMATICIANS NAMED **BABBAGE & LOVELACE,*** HAD GIVEN ME THE IDEA FOR A SORT OF **ARTIFICIAL BRAIN.**

*SEE PAGE **58.**

OR, AS I LIKED TO CALL IT, A **TURING MACHINE.** BUT UP TILL NOW, I'D ONLY BEEN ABLE TO **IMAGINE** HOW IT WOULD WORK...

NOW, WITH THE HELP OF THE BLETCHLEY TEAM, I SET OUT TO **BUILD** ONE!

THE GERMANS SENT SOME OF THE SAME TYPES OF MESSAGE EVERY DAY, SO WE COULD GUESS WHAT THEY SAID...

RAIN AGAIN

THEN WE COULD PLUG **THAT** INTO THE MACHINE, AND HAVE IT CHECK THE SETTINGS UNTIL IT FOUND A MATCH.

RAIN AGAIN

AND REMEMBER, ONCE WE FOUND THE SETTINGS FOR **ONE** MESSAGE, WE KNEW THE SETTINGS FOR **EVERY** MESSAGE SENT THAT DAY. THE MACHINES WERE SO VITAL THAT BY THE END OF THE WAR WE HAD OVER **200** OF THEM RUNNING AT THE SAME TIME!

CHK CHK CHK CHK CHK CHK CHK CHK CHK CHK CHK CHK CHK

WE WERE CRACKING NEW GERMAN MESSAGES SO FAST THAT WE COULD **QUITE LITERALLY** READ HITLER'S MAIL BEFORE **HE** DID!

AND THAT AMAZING ADVANTAGE MADE ALL THE DIFFERENCE IN WINNING THE WAR! YOU WERE A NATIONAL HERO!

ER, SORT OF...

YOU SEE, WE DIDN'T WANT THE GERMANS TO **REALISE** WE WERE READING THEIR MESSAGES. THEY'D HAVE CHANGED THEIR WHOLE SYSTEM AND WE'D BE BACK TO SQUARE ONE.

SO OF COURSE, WE COULDN'T TELL **ANYONE**. AND AFTER THE WAR IT REMAINED **TOP SECRET**.

AFTER THE WAR? BUT... WHY? IT'S NOT LIKE IT **MATTERED** ANY MORE **WHAT** THE GERMANS KNEW.

NO, BUT THE BRITISH GOVERNMENT SOLD A BUNCH OF CAPTURED ENIGMA MACHINES TO OTHER COUNTRIES, SO WE COULD READ **THEIR** SECRET MAIL!

YUP. **TOTALLY** UNBREAKABLE...

SO NO ONE **KNEW** HOW YOU'D HELPED WIN THE WAR AND SAVED **COUNTLESS** LIVES IN THE PROCESS?!

HEY — I DIDN'T NEED A MEDAL. IT WAS ENOUGH TO KNOW I'D HELPED.

I WAS MORE UPSET WHEN THEY DESTROYED ALL OUR BEAUTIFUL TURING MACHINES! BUT I WASN'T TOO WORRIED — I WAS ALREADY WORKING ON AN EVEN BETTER DESIGN...

YOU SEE, A TURING MACHINE LIKE THE ONE THAT CRACKED ENIGMA CAN ONLY DO **ONE** TASK. BUT I HAD THE IDEA FOR A MACHINE YOU COULD PROGRAM TO DO **ANY** TASK.

A **UNIVERSAL** TURING MACHINE.

OR, AS WE'D CALL IT TODAY, A **COMPUTER**.

EVERY COMPUTER SINCE HAS BEEN BUILT ON THE FOUNDATIONS OF YOUR GROUND-BREAKING WORK.

BUT, DESPITE THE FACT THAT YOU WERE BASICALLY **INVENTING THE FUTURE**, YOU DIDN'T LIVE TO SEE IT, DYING TRAGICALLY...

ALAN...?

HELLO...?

HOW ABOUT THAT! YOU CAN USE YOUR **TURING MACHINE** TO WATCH FUNNY VIDEOS OF **CATS**...

113

AN ENIGMA WRAPPED IN A MYSTERY

WITH THIS (SLIGHTLY SIMPLIFIED) ENIGMA MACHINE, YOU CAN SEND YOU OWN SUPER-SECURE SECRET CODE MESSAGES!

TO SEE HOW IT WORKS, LET'S **DECODE** A MESSAGE! FIRST, YOU'LL NEED THOSE ESSENTIAL CODEBREAKERS TOOLS: A **PEN AND PAPER!**

FIND THE FIRST LETTER OF THE SECRET MESSAGE.

THEN FOLLOW THE **COLOURED WIRE** FROM THAT LETTER THROUGH THE MAZE OF WIRES TO ITS **UNENCODED EQUIVALENT.**

WRITE DOWN THAT LETTER, THEN CONTINUE WITH THE REST OF THE MESSAGE (THIS ONE SAYS "U CANT READ THIS" — BUT NOW YOU CAN! HA HA!

TO **ENCODE** A SECRET MESSAGE JUST DO THE PROCESS IN REVERSE — PUT IN YOUR MESSAGE IN THE **BOTTOM** AND WRITE DOWN THE SCRAMBLED RESULT AT THE **TOP.**

THE REAL ENIGMA USED A SMALL NUMBER OF ROTATING COGS WHICH TURNED AFTER EACH LETTER, CHANGING THE WIRE CONNECTIONS.

THAT IS WHAT MADE IT SO HARD FOR US TO CRACK. BUT DON'T WORRY, EVEN **WITHOUT** MOVING PARTS, THIS ONE IS STILL PRETTY SECURE.

YOUR MESSAGE IS NOW **ENCRYPTED.** ONLY BY USING THE ENIGMA MACHINE IN **THIS VERY BOOK** WILL SOMEONE BE ABLE TO CRACK THE CODE!

UNLESS OF COURSE, THEY'VE GOT AN ENIGMA-CRACKING **TURING MACHINE** IN THEIR BASEMENT...

MY NEXT GUEST IS A MAN WHO NEEDS NO INTRODUCTION... BUT I'M GONNA GIVE HIM ONE ANYWAY!

IT'S THE MASSIVE **MEGA-GENIUS** WHOSE **MIND-BENDING** THEORIES **COMPLETELY REWROTE** THE LAWS OF SPACE AND TIME! PLEASE WELCOME...

ALBERT EINSTEIN!

ALBERT EINSTEIN
PHYSICIST
1879-1955

EINSTEIN, EVERYONE KNOWS YOU'RE AN INCREDIBLE GENIUS. BUT YOU WERE A TERRIBLE STUDENT AND YOU HATED SCHOOL. HOW IS THAT POSSIBLE?

IT WAS, I THINK, NOT ONLY POSSIBLE, BUT **NECESSARY!** I WAS SO CURIOUS TO UNDERSTAND THE WORLD, BUT SCHOOL SOUGHT ONLY TO **DRILL** ME TO MEMORISE **MEANINGLESS FACTS.**

BUT **ALL** MY GREAT DISCOVERIES CAME, NOT FROM FOLLOWING BLINDLY, BUT FROM WONDER, CURIOSITY AND ALLOWING MYSELF TO **THINK DIFFERENTLY**.

YOU WERE TRYING TO SOLVE SOME OF THE GREATEST PUZZLES OF SCIENCE, WHICH HAD ELUDED SCIENTISTS FOR CENTURIES!

I STUDIED IN MY SPARE TIME, AND THEN I WOULD GO FOR LONG WALKS. THAT WAS WHEN I DID MY **BEST THINKING!**

YOUR NEW THEORIES TURNED OUR UNDERSTANDING OF THE WORLD **UPSIDE DOWN!** CAN YOU EXPLAIN THEM TO US?

PEOPLE WERE **ALWAYS** ASKING ME THAT! I BECAME SO FAMOUS I COULDN'T WALK IN THE STREET WITHOUT **SOMEONE** STOPPING ME TO EXPLAIN MY THEORIES!

SO I DEVELOPED AN **ESCAPE PLAN**...

SO SORRY. WRONG GUY! PEOPLE ARE **ALWAYS** MISTAKING ME FOR THIS GUY EINSTEIN...

BUT I **KNOW** YOU'RE EINSTEIN! YOU CAN'T ESCAPE THIS TIME!

OK, OK. BUT I CAN'T EXPLAIN THE **WHOLE THING**. WE ONLY HAVE FOUR PAGES!

WELL, EVERYONE'S HEARD OF YOUR MOST FAMOUS EQUATION: $E=MC^2$! CAN YOU EXPLAIN **THAT**?

OK, SURE. THE **E** IS **ENERGY**, WHICH COULD BE LIGHT OR HEAT OR MOVEMENT — THINGS LIKE THAT.

THE M IS **MASS** — WHICH IS SORT OF LIKE WEIGHT OR SOLID-NESS.

THE $=$ WAS MY BIG DISCOVERY! BEFORE, SCIENTISTS THOUGHT THAT MASS AND ENERGY WERE DIFFERENT THINGS, BUT I REALISED THAT THEY ARE REALLY JUST TWO FORMS OF THE **SAME** THING!

AND THE C^2?

THAT'S THE SPEED OF LIGHT, MULTIPLIED BY ITSELF. BASICALLY, IT'S JUST A **REALLY, REALLY** BIG NUMBER.

WHAT, LIKE A MILLION?

A **BILLION**?

A **GAZILLION QUADRILLION**!?

BIGGER.

BIGGER THAN THAT.

THAT'S NOT A NUMBER...

LOOK, IT'S JUST **REALLY BIG**. SO, A **TINY** AMOUNT OF MASS CONVERTS INTO AN **ENORMOUS** AMOUNT OF ENERGY.

YOU'RE TALKING ABOUT A **NUCLEAR REACTION**. THIS IS THE THEORY BEHIND THE **ATOMIC BOMB**...

YES.

IF I HAD KNOWN WHERE IT WOULD ALL LEAD, I WOULD HAVE **TORN UP** MY THEORIES BEFORE ANYONE SAW THEM!

BECAUSE OF THE **AMAZING** AMOUNT OF ENERGY RELEASED IN A NUCLEAR REACTION, IT WOULD CREATE THE **BIGGEST EXPLOSION** THE WORLD HAD **EVER SEEN**!

I WAS ALWAYS OPPOSED TO ANY SORT OF WAR OR VIOLENCE, FOR **ANY** REASON...

BUT THEN, A YOUNG SCIENTIST WHO HAD ESCAPED FROM **HITLER'S GERMANY** WARNED ME THAT HITLER WAS TRYING TO DEVELOP AN ATOMIC BOMB!

I WROTE IMMEDIATELY TO THE PRESIDENT OF THE USA, URGING HIM TO BUILD A BOMB **FIRST**!

IT WAS THE GREATEST MISTAKE OF MY LIFE! AS IT TURNED OUT, WE DIDN'T NEED THE BOMB TO DEFEAT HITLER.

118

AMERICA WAS STILL FIGHTING WITH JAPAN, SO THEY DECIDED TO USE THE BOMB TO **TERRIFY** THE JAPANESE INTO SURRENDERING.

I WROTE TO THE PRESIDENT AGAIN, PLEADING WITH HIM **NOT** TO DROP IT ON JAPAN...

BUT THEY JUST COULDN'T RESIST TRYING IT OUT...

120,000 PEOPLE WERE **VAPORISED** INSTANTLY AND ANOTHER 65,000 DIED OF **BURNS** AND **RADIATION SICKNESS.**

I UNCOVERED THE BEAUTIFUL, PROFOUND SECRETS OF THE UNIVERSE, AND THEIR **FIRST APPLICATION** WAS THE MOST **HORRIFIC KILLING MACHINE** EVER DEVISED.

AND YET, YOU CARRIED ON WORKING!?

WHAT ELSE COULD I DO?! I DIDN'T BUILD THE BLASTED THING! AND ANYWAY, I STILL BELIEVE THAT KNOWLEDGE DOES MORE GOOD THAN EVIL.

ONE THING I REALISED IN MY STUDIES IS THAT, ALTHOUGH WE LIKE TO THINK THAT WE ARE **SEPARATE** FRIM THE REST OF THE UNIVERSE, THAT IS REALLY AN **ILLUSION.**

ONLY WHEN WE REALISE THAT WE ARE **ALL CONNECTED** WILL WE BE ABLE TO LIKE IN PEACE.

AAH!

OK, MAYBE NOT **THAT** CONNECTED...

It's all RELATIVE...

CORPSE TALK
Ground-Breaking
WOMEN

Adam & Lisa Murphy